Green is the Colou

hen tackling the mighty subject of John Deere and the company today you can only admire what has been achieved by them, sound products, quality build and above all investment for the future. One must also not forget in this world of takeovers, buyouts, mergers and dissemination that Deere & Co has seen all around it, the company is still its own entity and in this day and age that's something to be very proud of indeed. When you think of the company, green and the leaping deer come to mind straight away that's been created for so many years and I am proud to be associated with its tradition.

In some ways the colours used today by the company are basically similar to when tractor production took off with the purchase of the Waterloo Gasoline Engine Co, Waterloo, Iowa in 1918 and certainly stand out from the crowd. In this the 21st century these two elements are nothing but eco friendly to the environment we live in, which just shows how that famous

As an older man John Deere looks back at what he achieved as a Gilpin sulky plow is under test with the Moline works in the background.

individuality has kept the company ahead in so many ways. That very much stems from the 'New Generation' which, was put on line in 1960 some 50 years ago and as other companies floundered John Deere has not looked back since.

Moving on in time other tractor companies had labour problems particularly in the 70s and 80's. It just got better for Deere a steady hand and working hand in hand with the unions has certainly paid dividends for the company and staff alike they are all proud to be part of that John Deere tradition. Agriculture and farming are very much an up and down game and going with the flow of things has been a key factor for the success of the company as well keeping something in the bank just in case has always being a wise decision at times.

Life was very tough for John Deere when he started out particularly with the loss of his father at a young age when on his return journey from his father land Great Britain to Vermont, USA. John Deere lived in the crowded state of Vermont in those formative and he had a lot of failure early on but he kept his head high and battled through and didn't rely on others. After he travelled east to Grand Detour, Illinois in 1937 he started to repair his freind Leonard Andrus broken pitman shaft in his saw mill one of his first jobs, he was told about the problems of the sticky soil and finding a plough to break the land up satisfactory.

Thinking about the smooth surface of the pit saw (two handed) he fathomed a simple hard surface but polished steel plough mouldboard that did the trick and set him and his family on their way to success. In fact that very

Peter Love visited Frog Hollow, Middlebury Vermont where JD had his last forge before he headed west.

first original plough still exists at the Smithsonian Institute, Washington. John Deere was not a great inventor as such, but a great organiser, reliable and his enthusiasm knew no bounds. In fact just to show what good products the company made they introduced a steal-beam walking plough in 1867 that was still in demand during the 1940's.

That reliability and strength of depth gives Deere & Co something very special which is shared by all those who work and use John Deere equipment today, long shall it remain so.

All I have to add is sit back and enjoy this ground breaking book that is certainly different in its way to what you have come across before.

Very lastly I dedicate this work to Don Macmillan the father of John Deere in the UK when it comes to preservation and the 'New Generation.' ∎

Peter Love

The Green Giant 1912 - 2010

Published by

KELSEY PUBLISHING GROUP

Printed in England, United Kingdom by William Gibbons
of Willenhall, West Midlands
on behalf of
Kelsey Publishing Limited,
Cudham Tithe Barn,
Cudham, Kent TN16 3AG
Telephone: 01959 541444   Fax: 01959 541400
www.kelsey.co.uk

©2010
ISBN 978-1-907426-06-3

With thanks to:
Peter Love, Jayne Love Lynn Davies, Andrew Hall, Scott Lambert, Joseph Lewis,
Chris McCullough, Howard Sherren, Peter D Simpson, Peter Squires.
Also a big thank to the owners of all these fine tractors featured.

Contents

Original 1924 'Spoker' D

JOHN DEERE

1924 Model "D"

SER 30818

JAKE & SHARON RENS
ORANGE CITY, IOWA

A tremendous amount of experimentation went into the D 15-27 before it came on stream in 1923 when 50 were built (30401-304510). The tractor proved to be a solid performer in the 3-furrow plough sector and was a match for all including the IHC 15-30. From number 30451 full production started in 1924 and ended at 191670 in 1953, which makes the D the longest production tractor ever, but not the most produced.

In 1924 some 764 were made including this example 30618 with the 26in (66cm) 'Spoker' flywheel this was reduced in size to 24in (61cm) from 31280 with provision for power take off in the casing. From December 1925 36249 the solid flywheel replaced the spoke flywheel and was to stay to the end with modifications over the years.

To find a tractor like Jake and Sharon Ren's from Orange City, Iowa is exceptional and it runs as well as it looks and was seen in 2008 at Waterloo, Iowa just a short distance from where it had been made 84 years before.

Photo: Peter Love

Seen at Tractor World for the first time in the public eye together are the John Deere GP Series 1 and 5, look at all the differences starting with the clutch levers.

Waterloo Brothers

Peter Love talks with his friend Bill Cowley about his GP Series 1 and his just restored GP Series 5 that debuted at Tractor & Machinery's Tractor World Show in 2009.

On its way from Nebraska to a new life in the UK some five years ago now is GP 229267, it looks in good order, but hours of work would see it right.

ohn Deere introduced the Model C in the high summer of 1927 as an answer to the 1923 IHC Farmall Regular rowcrop. For International the Farmall sales were disappointing at first, but started taking off, and in 1926 they sold some 4,400 units. In 1927 they were making 300 of this range per week, yes you did read that correctly. John Deere realised it needed to get into this market.

The key to the C, or All Crop as it was first called by Theo Brown head of the JD experimental department and board member, was the power lift. This could raise and lower the integral cultivator and three-row plough, besides other implements. As we all know eventually this would revolutionise farming, but it was to take

some time getting. Quite simply John Deere were in a rush to get a tractor out there to compete against the 'dreaded' red in this growing field of rowcrop agriculture. To fit a tractor within a set up like this it had to be a short wheel base machine, hence instead of an overhead valve engine as used on the larger and popular D, Brown went for a side-valve unit, which was a mistake. Some five experimental models were created in three and four wheel configuration. However after field tests it was decided that a longer wheelbase tractor in standard configuration was really required.

In the early spring of 1927 some 25 standard tractors had been assembled and were shipped for testing across the USA. At the time it's noted that they were referred to on the paperwork as the C and not so much the All Crop. Apparently they had gone down very well with the

farmers and a number of improvements were asked for, particularly connected to the imprecise steering, and work was on going with the implements, particularly the cultivator. In fact the steering box was totally repositioned in the centre of the tractor and the long draglink was worked from the right hand side and not the left as previously, but they kept the wooden steering wheel.

The two-cylinder engine was rather under powered for the size of tractor at 20hp, but with a new governor, lubrication system and more tuning things were on the up. Further work on the power lift and pto had seen this combined together on the tractor; it was all a race against time. By autumn 1927 tentative production had started with 76 units being assembled at first. All in all some 99 units were to be made under the title of model C and many of them were to be totally recreated at Waterloo when the ongoing

In May 1930 starting with 222345 a few GP's received the larger 'square' 6in bore engine and crossover intake/exhaust manifolds. From January 1931 (224100) all the engine improvements had been incorporated.

The Series 5 GP featured improved final drives, larger cooling capacity, fuel tank and air filter.

The first GP with Firestone pneumatic tyres on French and Hecht wheels was number 229110.

The Ensign 'K' carburettor was rather fragile and 'touchy' and was replaced in 1934 with the far superior Marvel-Schebler DLTX-5 from 229363.

The 1931 modifications included lowering the compression ratio, this was compensated by the .25 increased bore and a larger capacity radiator from 226402.

development had been completed. In fact most of the C's ended up as GP's, however a few slipped through the net and one that lasted in original configuration is 200109 that has lasted into preservation times, probably because as it was produced first.

Full production, with many updates, started in the autumn of 1928, but by now the C name had been dropped in favour of calling the new tractor the GP. It was Frank Silloway the JD sales manager who said that people were getting confused when ordering a C or the D tractor so the General Purpose GP sounded a lot better and it stuck. The GP started at 200211 not 200111 as quoted in some correspondence.

Before moving on to the GP however one has to say that Theo Brown's C was the first tractor in the world, it is said, to offer four sources of power from one unit, pto, drawbar, belt pulley and of course

that power lift. Although an option, the power lift made this tractor a success story and was used principally not only on the GP, but the 1928-29 GP Tricycle and its replacement the 1928-33 GPWT (wide track).

During those early years of the problematical GP 5.75 x 6in side-valve engine, the air cleaner design and position wasn't good. It became clogged up very quickly, stopped air flow which effected performance, and if not looked after could cause engine failure eventually. In fact Deere & Co were very good over claims and certainly kept their customers happy. It took a while to get around to sorting this air cleaner problem out and from 212555 a new vertical (above the bonnet) air cleaner and pipe was fitted in 1929 on the o/s.

As you can see the GP went through a lot with its development and that was not to change. Some 68 GP's were built in May 1930

with the larger 6 x 6in 'square' side-valve engine and a new manifold arrangement, which was to be modified yet again in 1931. The new improved tractor finally got going in production at the very end of December 1930, but further improvements happened in 1931 as well. Yet again a new air cleaner arrangement was created; the exhaust gained a silencer and a tall exhaust pipe. To help on the maintenance side of things the oil system gained an easy to change oil filter on the crankcase and the final drive was redeveloped. Later on in 1931 a new larger radiator and sides came along with a slightly smaller capacity fuel tank. Further improvements followed, but not the overhead valve cylinder head that was really required. Yet pneumatic tyres made the greatest difference to the tractor and to all makers who took them up early on. For the GP they came along ➡

The steering was totally overhauled by Bill during the restoration and new French and Hecht wheels were obtained.

A Fairbanks Morse R2 magneto was standard throughout the GP production run 1928-35.

When the new 'square' engine came in the radiator was changed from mid 1931 (C1940R) with new radiator cast sides (C1910/1).

Standing up was standard practice on pre 1945 'tractoring' throughout the world.

GP Series 1-5

Series 1-2 - Both with side-valve 5.75 x 6in bore and stroke water injection 5111cc 17.24dhp – 24.97bhp engine, all with three-speed transmission.

1928-29 Series 1 - Looks the same as the C, but carries a cast metal steering wheel, n/s oblong exhaust stub, axle stops (front), spring steal seat support and 'General Purpose' decals. Large fuel tank, screw caps, cast steering wheel and flat wheel spokes on front.

1929-30 Series 2 - Similar to above, but with the cross over vertical air intake pipe on the outside o/s (from 212555), new style round spoke wheels on front - in fact there were at least another five front wheel designs used during the life of the GP period.

1931-2 Series 3 - Now with 6 x 6in 5553cc square engine 18.86dhp – 25.36bhp. The compression was lowered, without water injection, new crank bearings, crossover manifold with air intake through the bonnet.

1932-33 Series 4 - N/s air inlet and o/s upright exhaust and new front wheels.

1933-5 Series 5 - Pneumatic tyres standard, new carburettor and Vortox air cleaner.

Technical specification

1928	1112
1929	11,635
1930	10,676
1931	4816
1932	384
1933	167
1934	1252
1935	232
Total	30,274

in late 1932 and they gradually became standard, and not just an option.

Having enjoyed his Series 1 for a good number of years Bill came to hear about a 1934 Series 5 229267 that belonged to Steve Just from Funk, Nebraska, which just had to come back to the UK. The Series 5 was to be an 'off and on job' over the years for Bill and according to the original specification sheet the tractor had been supplied with pneumatics, but during its life steel wheels had been fitted on. He searched out a set of the original style French and Hecht wheels with new tyres going on the front wheels. Mechanically the tractor was in excellent condition, but after pulling the flat head off it revealed burnt valves and seats. The bores and bottom end where found to be in excellent order as was the radiator. New oils were

the order of the day followed by a new head gasket and repairs to the valves and seats. With it all bolted back together again, the tractor fired up in fine order. The Fairbanks Morse R2 magneto was in excellent condition. A new axle centre pin and steering king pins and bushes were overhauled. The transmission was found to be in good order, but the brake clutches were overhauled and relined along the way.

After a sand blast using Vapormatic synthetic paints, a company which is actually owned by John Deere today, Bill finished the tractor off with three top coats of JD green. One has to remember that the pre-war green used by this company is darker than that used today. By November 2008 the job was complete, the Series 5 was ready to go and as Bill reversed the tractor into the garage where

it joined its earlier 1928 Series 1 brother for the first time in a completed state.

They make a most interesting pair, their differences are many and fascinating to discover. Production of the semi-successful GP, which had somewhat dented JDs reputation, had certainly been brought into line after all the 1931 modifications. The last example was completed on 4th March 1935, number 230745 and was shipped to Fredericksburg, Texas on 18th March. Over 30,000 GP's had been made and it was positive evidence that JD was here to stay in the rowcrop business. JD had learnt so much from the GP and was to use that experience to dominate this side of the agricultural market over the next 40 years at least. This started with the model that replaced the GP, the Model A rowcrop, but that's another story… ■

Preservation in motion

Restoration expert Nigel Burgess tells the story of rebuilding Henry Dixon's prize-winning 1944 John Deere BW.

What a picture of beauty, the 1944 John Deere BW finished second in the concours class at Tractor World, Malvern in March 2005 which is remarkable since this tractor is still used!

The example shown here dates from August 2, 1944 (the tractor plate number cannot be read properly) and is the most common type in the UK, being a wartime Lease Lend import, and came from North Yorkshire at one time. The B signifies the model and the W stands for wide front axle. Even though there were 104, 247 six-speed Bs produced, there were only 1,387 BWs produced and just 266 in 1944. The BW could be regarded as a good restoration project as they are not common in the USA.

A materials saving exercise was adopted during WWII and in 1942 the steel chassis was changed to cast iron and the copper radiator was changed to a pressurised steel radiator (148500-166999). An enthusiast can spot the change by the pressurised radiator cap. However, from 149700 the PTO shaft was increased to 1 3/8in. Further savings were made with regard to rubber in the fan assembly, when steel friction discs were fitted as used on the Model D. Restoration

On first look, the BW seemed in good running order but all the usual areas of wear and tear for a tractor of this age were present. As the 14dbh engine ran so well, and the power and pressures were all deemed satisfactory, it was not necessary to undertake a full restoration. Various initial road tests indicated that the transmission was satisfactory, too, so this left creature comforts and wearing points to be returned to their original state.

CLUTCH MECHANISM

The clutch mechanism is a typical wear point on all JD two-cylinder tractors and so repairs were undertaken to correct the problem. Basically, it's a bushing and building-up exercise. First of all, the bottom half of the clutch fork shaft is splined and if you are unlucky these can be worn. The easiest option is to find another fork where the splines are good. However the plain top half of the fork is normally worn and measures one inch diameter to match the splines. Some people turn the shaft down and chrome it back to the original size. Another method is to braze the shaft and then turn it down on a lathe to the original diameter, using the original centres.

The fork housing will also be worn, so a surface plate was made that mounts on the housing to fit the milling machine used. This is important to achieve a precise position. Use a boring bar that passes through the full length of the housing (most of the wartime Bs have a core plug in the bottom of the housing that you can knock out for the bar to pass through). If you have a housing that does not have the core plug you can manufacture a spacer and a shorter boring bar to use as a guide. ➡

As everything should be thousanth-perfect, you need the right tool for the right job. With the housing bored out, a steel bush was made back to 1in. Steel bushes are used instead of bronze because otherwise both surfaces will be soft and will wear, so you'll be back to the beginning. The pulley brake, again, is a matter of boring out and re-bushing to complement the rest of the mechanism. The hardest part of this operation is holding the piece in a secure position. However, with the aid of clamps and spacers this can be achieved and a good job done. The pulley brake pad also wears and you can change these with an aftermarket pad, or if you want to go the whole hog you can re-rivet a pad direct onto the housing.

There's nothing worse than a loose clutch handle, and don't be fooled into thinking that just buying a JD bush will do the job. The pins can also be worn so these were re-manufactured and knurled to ensure that they don't rotate in the tractor mount. Beware when removing the pins that you don't snap off the casting from the tractor. It is best to use heat and a puller instead of snapping one through rushing the job. Remount the adjustable connecting rod and make some oversize clevis pins to keep it all tight.

Compared to some tractors the BW looked in good condition, but looks can deceive.

When buying any rowcrop tractor, make sure the axle splines are in good order or it can take a lot of effort to rebuild them, and at a high cost too.

The two-cylinder 19bhp engine certainly has clean lines; the plug leads are placed inside the loom, which helps to protect the plugs from damage.

The 'new' John Deere A and B brochure dating from 1947, when the pressed frame was introduced.

MODEL B TIMELINE

Said to be the last unstyled John Deere BWH Hi-crop, number 58095 was built on June 8, 1938. The first one had been built in December 1937(51679), both were shipped to California.

1935 John Deere Model B rowcrop unstyled type tractor introduced for smaller farmers who require a general purpose tractor. A good platform with four speeds, the rowcrop basic features are an adjustable wheel tread, ample vision and clearance, convenient controls and the steering having individual brakes. The tractor is rated at 11.84dhp-16.01bhp.

1938 Styled Bs produced from late 1938, but sold from 1939. The two-cylinder engine increased from 149ci to 175ci (14dhp-19bhp). Four-speed transmission and rear end used until 1941 and the unstyled fuel tank fitted underneath the new styling. After serial number 96000 a new six-speed transmission is introduced to keep up with the demands of modern farming. Some 16 styles of B were on offer.

1947 The chassis is replaced with a pressed steel design. A new front axle configuration is introduced, and a fine cushion seat for the driver, while the engine is increased to 190ci. The Majority of the Bs were straight gas (petrol), and power increases to 24dhp-28bhp. Controls re-designed to improve ease of use.

1952 The B finishes production with 306,282 produced in total. They transmuted to the numbered series, but the principle of the design did not finish until the beginning of the 1960s, and was carried on even longer elsewhere in the world.

What a picture! Painted in 1945 by artist Walter Haskell Hinton for John Deere – 'V for Victory.'

Here we see the face plate made up to hold the clutch housing on the milling machine base.

With everything set level the milling machine bores the housing oversize, before the steel bushes (not bronze) are fitted, then reamed to size.

The clutch shaft, is a place that most two-cylinder John Deere's wear badly – if the splines are still good there are various methods of building the shaftup and turning it back to the original size

It certainly was not easy to hold the housing in a secure position as it was bored out; small cuts were taken at a time!

Look at the state of the clutch brake lining, and those very worn pin holes which are oblong.

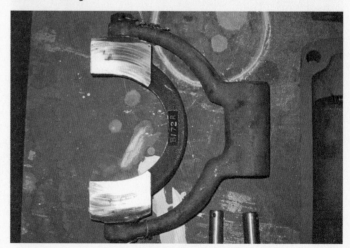

The clutch thrust and fork assembled, rebushed, ready to go and all wired up.

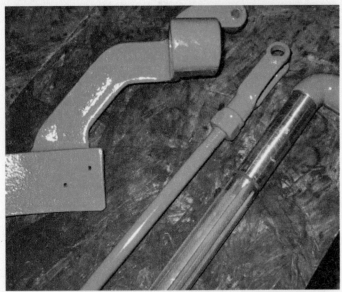

Ready to be greased and refitted, it might not look like a lot of work, but this had taken over 20 hours work.

All assembled and ready to be tested in the housing, a coat of protective paint will be applied before final assembly.

Nearly complete and reassembled on the tractor, where the operation would be tested, before final fitment.

Adjusting the clutch can take some time, but it is worth it in the end, how many tractor drivers do you hear crunching the gears?

ADJUSTING THE CLUTCH

When adjusting the clutch it is important to pull the clutch handle back towards the operator, then loosen off the adjusting screw and lock nut on the pulley brake. This then is well out of the way and will not encroach during the adjusting procedure. Tighten up the three castle nuts until they are all firm, and then, using a socket and ratchet, loosen off each castle nut an even amount in turn. Proceed with this until the clutch handle goes forward into the

engaged position with a distinctive snap – about 40-80lb of pressure (Models A, B and H) and 100lb of pressure (Models D and G). This is approximately a turn and a half. You can then go a quarter of a turn or so each way to achieve the definitive click. Then tighten up the adjusting screw on the pulley brake until you see the clutch handle start moving forward.

When this is done tighten up the lock nut. If you haven't got the range you will have to screw it in and out according

A full set of the correct transfers are essential for any good John Deere restoration.

to the rod and yoke. This is important because the main reason why the clutch assembly is not working in the first place is because the pulley brakes are tightened

A good set of original type tyres is essential for any good restoration. Cleaning them before a show issomething that has to be given attention these days.

How it all began - somewhat different to its present day fully restored condition!

Making its first appearance; at the Stoneleigh International Festival in June 2004. The tractor was certainly a wonderful sight, and has since been on road runs and other events in Wales with its owner Henry Dixon.

up too much. When pulling back on the clutch arm you force the mechanism and incur wear because most operators want to stop the tractor by using the clutch rather than the foot brake.

ADJUST BRAKES

Adjusting the brakes comes before you start the road test for obvious reasons. To do this job properly, it is best to jack up each side of the tractor individually, turn the square adjuster right up then back off a quarter of a turn at a time until the rear wheel can be rotated by hand. The clutch should already be adjusted by now (see part 2 in June 2005 *T&M*– order back issues on page 26). However, after a good run and with everything settled in you may need to tighten up a turn,so to speak, on both the clutch and the brakes.

THE FINISHED ARTICLE

Well there you have it! If you've followed the restoration over the last three months, you may be wondering how many hours it took to complete in real-time. Nigel explains that the total time was around 585 hours with the help of his partner Debs Cornwell. Hopefully some of you will be thinking of undertaking a John Deere restoration. If so, one final word of advice: many of the John Deeres imported to the UK in recent years are the ones that the American and Canadian collectors don't want! Do look very carefully when thinking of purchasing one… ∎

Brute Force

Ian Pierce out and about with his 1945 John Deere D at Tingley's Trundle in October 2003.

Mark H Hughes travelled to the East Sussex coast during the heavy January storms in 2004 to meet one of Southern England's pioneer collectors, Ian Pierce.

Mark had come to see his fabulous styled 1945 John Deere D that debuted at the SCHVPT Ardingly show back in July 1982, and looks just as good today as that hot weekend in 1982.

I asked Ian why is the John Deere D so special? "Well, like me it goes on forever!" The D had the longest production run of any tractor - 1923-1953. The tractor just would not go away even when John Deere wanted it to and had its replacement model in production, the 1949 model R 50.96bhp

diesel. In fact the last 91 Ds (191579-191670), commonly known as 'Streeters', were assembled outside the Waterloo factory between the mill room and the truck shop, as there was no room in the inn!

YOUTHFUL MEMORIES

The truth of the matter for Ian though is that as a boy at Priest Hall Farm, Stone Cross, Eastbourne, East Sussex, he well remembers a 1943 styled D working. On the rack saw bench in the very early 1950s they put on a more modern Nuffield N4 with Perkins power. Here the tractor was expected to saw through a huge hulk of oak, after all it was the latest British diesel-powered machine. Unfortunately the tractor couldn't hack it and stalled! Once the D was attached the 42bhp Waterloo built tractor

did the trick, yes it did splutter a bit as the governors slowly opened but the petrol/paraffin JD was something to be counted on, and made no other fuss whatsoever. Ian's memories certainly qualify what farmers and operators of the time came to know and love about the D - it was reliable and could do the job in hand. Ian says this was not the first D Lease- Lend tractor that had been at Priest Hall Farm, Stone Cross, the first example with hand start only was destroyed in a mysterious electrical fire.

JR Hobbs, America's most respected of writers on John Deere matters, expressed another example of the magnitude of the performance of a D. He tells the story of an owner of a styled D that worked day in, day out in heavy soil conditions and wanted to move into the modern era.

The tractor that started it all off for Ian was the 1943 D at Stone Cross, which in later life was used for 12-bore shotgun target practice by many local lads. It was later saved for preservation, and was brought back to running order, but leaked water into the bores overnight. It was owned by Win Wood, it then passed into Arthur Tingley's hands who swapped a Farmall for it. He then moved it on with another swap for an Oliver 70, it then moved to Cumbria by all accounts, where is it now!

The chateau where the tractor came from in the Rhone Alps of south-central France.

Now all loaded and ready to come home to England.

He set his son off on the D with a 3-14 plough behind. Father casually adjusted the mounted 3-14 plough behind a brand new 1965 JD 3020 82hp diesel. Quite naturally he thought it would not be long before he would catch his son up and pass him on the 3020. How wrong he was! The torque of that old D in the heavy soil conditions proved the winner! As JR goes on to say, the farmer was not happy with his new machine and was straight on the phone to the JD salesman who promptly sent out a 94hp 4020. Apparently word got around and not many 3020s were sold in the area!

As you can see, the Model D is renowned the world over, and it was a particularly popular tractor in Canada, the largest export market for the model.

FINDING A JD 'D'
I asked Ian how he acquired his Model D? "That's a long story," he said. He has had a lifelong interest in farm machinery, like his good friend Tony Baker; they both worked for Marlow Ropes at Hailsham, who happened to have a depot in Calais, France.

Ian wrote to Marshalls at Gainsborough asking did they know where he could acquire a Field-Marshall Series 3A? They wrote and said they didn't have any in stock, but the main export markets were Australia, South Africa, New Zealand and France.

That got Tony and Ian thinking; and they put an advert in the French equivalent of Farmers Weekly, giving Marlow Ropes' French address as the contact. This produced a whole raft of Field-Marshalls tractors that came out of the woods, and eventually the team brought back six tractors between them in the late 1970s. Both restored an example each, and to high standards indeed. Ian's example departed some years ago, but Tony's example remained in his fold until 2002. They also set Ian Parrett on the road to finding Marshall MP6s and others this Somerset dealer was to bring back in time.

OVER TO FRANCE WE GO!
However Ian was very keen to obtain a John Deere D, especially from France as they had not got the tractor 'bug' yet and they thought people interested in such things were crazy! Eventually Ian got some response, but he didn't quite get the numbers he obtained for the

Field-Marshall adverts, turning up just a couple. The most interesting was based at a chateau at Vaugirard Barge, near Mount Brison in the Rhone Alps, south-central France. Things were arranged in the summer of 1979, and Ian and his wife Ann took their Renault 5 via the Newhaven ferry to see the D. They camped along the way of the 1,000-mile trip. They didn't have any problems finding the premises, which trained and bred racing horses. They were taken to see the D, which had been parked in the barn for years! There was even a chicken's egg on the tractor's platform! However the tractor was very straight indeed, the wings showed no rust and the tyres were amazing! That particular D, number 161047, had been made in 1945 and had been imported under the Marshall Plan. It had electrics and lights as well, and the early dynamo system, which we will come to later.

Ian established the tractor's engine was free and very complete indeed. By the sieve screen on the grille and by interpretation it was deduced that originally a local threshing contractor had used the D for a number of seasons, before combines took over. It was later sold to the chateau who hardly used it. Ian reckons it had done less than 3,000 hours, remarkable for any French tractor, They are normally 'hacked to death' as described by one owner of a number of French JDs, who had to replace crankshafts, con rods and even axles in the restoration process.

After the examination it was down to the bar for the financial negotiations to start, which were not concluded straight away. Ian and Ann returned to the UK not knowing if they were going to be able to afford to buy the D. Eventually things were concluded at a cost to Ian of 500 francs (£50), yes you did read that right! ➡

The new styled Henry Dreyfuss designed John Deere D, the third one to be completed for the company by him and his team.

The tractor is making good progress in the workshop. This picture shows the rear end looking forward, and those enormous wheel hubs that John Deere used.

It's May 1980 and just months away from completion, the unit construction design is clearly seen.

The two-cylinder power house and the valve cover is clearly seen, it's always best to run the engine up and adjust the tappets before replacing the radiator again, and check for oil leaks.

The flywheel side of the D is seen here, with the fuel tank in place, all being restored in a small garage.

The two pistons shine in the workshop light, the cylinder head was nearly ready to be refitted.

Now with the money changed hands, collecting the tractor had to be sorted out, as not many people toured to the part of France where the tractor stood. It turned out that an old pal of the editor, Peter Denham a keen tractor collector himself, at the time worked for a company who took caravans each week to St Tropez. It was going to be a tight schedule for this popular gentleman, who incidentally is racing a 1968 Merlin MkII these days in Classic Formula Ford.

COLLECTING THE TRACTOR
On February 12, 1980, Ian met Peter at Dover and the week-long venture began! It is a story in itself; they delivered the caravans and arrived at the chateau to collect the D, a job that needed to be done ASAP as time was short with a boat to catch some 500 miles away. However when they arrived it was all hands to the deck as a difficult birth of a foal was taking place. Ian and Peter spent hours drinking French coffee in this massive chateau all on their own! When this was concluded the master of the house for sentimental reasons wanted to see the D running, which really didn't interest Ian at this stage, but he reluctantly agreed. After the plugs were cleaned, the magneto points were checked, cleaned, gapped and refitted, fuel was delivered to the Marvel-Schebler DLTX- 16 carburettor, so by the looks of things it might possibly start.

The decompression taps were opened and Ian spun the flywheel over, and do you know what? The D started, something it hadn't done for 25 or so years! The man of the house was ecstatic - it was time for celebration, but the team did not have any spare time - they were already six hours late.

In the end they left Vaugirard Barge at 2pm and made the docks at Calais just before midnight. After a considerable amount of customs formalities, the tractor arrived in East Sussex at 8pm Saturday night; it had certainly been an unforgettable experience, and one that Ian recalls with pleasure!

RESTORATION ASSESSMENT
Ian says when you go to buy a tractor evaluate in your own mind how much it will cost to restore, and if you have any doubts just walk away and move on. However, Ian knew that all the extra efforts to bring the tractor home had been worth it. The tractor ran, the clutch was not seized and the three-speed gearbox selectors were not worn. This is something that is a problem in the case of quite a few John Deeres after years of much exertion and torture beyond the call of duty. Ian recently read that a fellow JD owner was to restore a four-speed D, well as Ian says 'there ain't such a thing.' The D started out as a two-speed tractor in 1923 and was upped to three-speed in 1935 from serial number 119945.

Mind you this is one of the problems with owning a D, the gear ratios are very low and on a road run you need a head start. First gear gives 2.25mph, second 3.25 and third 5mph. However, Ian did say they actually do a bit more than that but not much, you can see why they don't wear out. For ploughing and threshing this tractor couldn't be beaten, particularly in its time; that two-cylinder 8,206cc ohv engine producing 38dbh/42bhp was truly something.

From the point of view of maintenance and restoration the simple design is a winner. The unit-construction D does not have a frame to hold the engine and housings in like other JDs of the time. This all helps to get around the tractor with ease, a major plus when working in a small suburban garage. Another consideration is the tractor's short wheelbase of 130in and a low height of 61in, again a plus for storage, however one does need good garage footings as they weigh 5,270lb, so be careful when jacking it up! When you have restored a D you certainly have the granddaddy of all John Deeres, and something of creditable future value.

The first JD that 'Mr John Deere' (Don Macmillan) purchased for his contracting business in the 40s was this styled D, which is seen in action!

DOING THE WORK

As soon as the tractor arrived back in the UK, Ian was straight on the job; he took off the Henry Dreyfuss-designed tinwork introduced in 1939 (from number 143800 onwards). He then removed the cylinder head to find out his fate, and to his surprise all was good, the bores showed hardly any wear and didn't even need a hone out. Decoking the cylinder head and regrinding the valves was just a formality. The radiator and the top and bottom tanks were cleaned out, new gaskets made and reassembled. Various other things were gone through and adjusted, but nothing significant at all was replaced on the major mechanical items, and the brakes were in fine order, particularly the linings.

PAINTWORK

The 'beast' was then stripped down and sand blasted, mindful of covering up the major components where sand could cause major problems in the future. As we said earlier all the panels had been removed for this job. It is essential to pressure wash and remove all the grime and grease before this operation starts.

In 1981 two-pack paints and the like were only just coming in, and enamel paints were still the 'in thing.' International Paints were very much 'the' company at the time, and Ian advises using one paint system and stick with it. After red oxide was applied on the raw castings and bright metal of the panels, it was time to add a bit of Davids Isopon P38 filler where small dents were

spotted in the panels. Lots of primer filler was applied using the International system, lots of time was needed to thoroughly dry each coat or problems would occur later. This was a problem - the editor had nightmares with one of his restorations in 1979 using this paint system.

However Ian had this all under control and said that the success of good solid paintwork comes with rubbing the paintwork down, particularly at this stage; he applied at least 10 coats. Then it was one light coat followed with two full coats of International John Deere green, and one has to say it turned out very well. Ian says that John Deere's own present-day green paint is not the same colour as used in the 1940s. Then the colour was slightly darker with a touch more chrome yellow in the paint, so beware!

WHEELS AND TYRES

Treble B Tyres at Hailsham removed the original 1945 Goodyear tyres from the wheel rims so Ian could paint them. The fitter said the pink inner tubes were better quality than the present-day examples available! The spoked French & Hecht type pneumatic rear wheel rims were replaced with heavy cast rims with the introduction of the styled D in April 1939. These 28in rims (D2570R) were fitted on numbers 143800-150616. The Ds that had the option of rear wheel brakes naturally used a different cast rim (D2512R), numbers 143800-15956, again these were 28in diameter. As from 1941, number 150617, the rim size was changed to 30in diameter (D3120R). Again, if the tractor had wheel

brakes like Ian's example a different 30in rim was used (D3135R). Turning to the front wheels, the round spoke 7.50 x 18 front wheels were phased out in 1944 and the pressed steel front wheels (JD1267J) came in from 159011 until the end in 1953.

Even though the front and rear wheels were in good order, it always takes some hard work to make them, into good order. Again lots of coats of paint were applied, but lots of hard rubbing is the key feature here, and Ian cannot emphasise this enough, using wet and dry 320 grade paper for a start, followed with 400- 600 grade paper before applying a light top coat, then another light rub of 800 grade. Then lots of dusting down, and water on the floor, before applying the final top coats, that have been on the tractor ever since!

"If you do it right it will last!" Ian says and he has certainly proved it some 21 years later. While the rims were being sorted out, the tyres were cleaned and made good, these original 1945 tyres are still on the tractor today! However do build up the wheels before the final paint coats are applied or it will cause much anguished with chipped rims later on.

ELECTRICS

The electrics turned out to be the area of concern for Ian. John Deere were still learning about them in 1939 when they were introduced on the D. The 6 volt system had the dynamo (generator in JD terms) on the nearside and anchored to a cast bracket taken from the governor housing (tractor ➡

Late in the evening the completed tractor emerges from the garage to the pleasure of many.

nos:143800-161399). It was not well designed at all, and the cast bracket regularly broke. Ian's D was typical of this and a new one was cast during the rebuild The crossed 'V' belt was, and is, a nightmare to fit. However in late 1945 (number 161400 on) this arrangement was moved to the offside, precluding the continual problems of fitting the belt and the dynamo bracket breaking.

For Ian one of the big plusses was the Don Macmillan disposal sale in Wiltshire. Here he acquired a new dynamo, starter solenoid and heater gauge. He found a pair of sidelights just by chance at the EHVPC's annual spring autojumble at Eastbourne, and he paid only £10 for the pair of beautiful Sims lamps. The headlamp was obtained and the only thing that was missing was the flywheel ring gear guard, which John Deere had on the shelf, even though the tractor had been out of production for 28 years!

The day came for the tractor to make its debut at the 'hot' July 1982 Southern Counties Historic Vehicle Preservation Trust rally at the South of England Showground, Ardingly, Sussex. The tractor was admired but didn't pick up a prize at the show. However days later the D appeared at the much more prestigious Kent Show where vintage tractors are fully appreciated. Here Ian came away with 'Best In Class', presented to him by Lady Astor of Hever Castle. Considering the tractor commentator was a salesman for Drake & Fletcher, then agents for John Deere, the three-day show had turned out to be something very special indeed, one that Ian even today exhibits at on occasions. From that day on the tractor has appeared at a number of shows, but has never been extensively

rallied, partly because a problem developed that would bug the D for over 20 years!

It was only a year or so after the restoration that the tractor started to give problems. It just would not start with any ease - the Edison Splitdorf CD magneto (fitted on tractors 143800-152707, then 153209-155599 and 155600-187102) had been overhauled professionally, so surely it couldn't be that? In the process of all of this the nearside Marvel-Schelbler DLTX-16 carburettor would flood and that would be that for at least a couple of hours! Somehow this became a major problem, and the tractor was pushed to the back of the shed as Ian restored other tractors and built his current house.

It was in 2001 Ian decided that he had got to do something about it, and went to see Palmers of Lower Dicker, Hailsham the local JD dealers. He was thinking about purchasing a Wico X magneto - these were fitted on the very last of the Ds (187103- 191670) and was such a thing available? To his surprise JD Waterloo had 20 in stock and two at Mannheim, the company's European manufacturing HQ in Germany.

Within 48 hours it had arrived at Lower Dicker and was awaiting collection, on it said "Standard Magneto Company, Chicago." The £300 or so was well worth it, particularly as Ian's old Edison Splitdorf CD magneto was in demand. The next day the Wico X was on and timed up. The tractor started first pull of the starter button; it was just like that day in France 32

years before when the 'brute force' tractor fired up so easily for Ian. As the capable D owner says, the answer to these tractors is a strong and bright spark, in fact the engine note is much more rhythmic and smother today than ever before - "It's the best money I have ever spent in years!"

For Ian John Deere tractors are number one, and this D epitomises his youth and the example he remembers at Stone Cross all those years ago. "It's all pure nostalgia," he says, "and I enjoy every minute of the hobby even today, nearly 40 years from when I first got involved." ∎

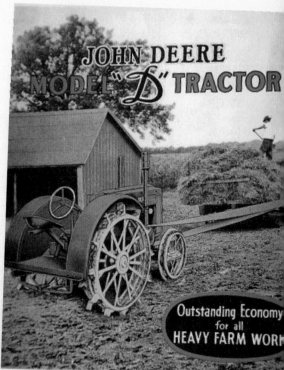

Ronnie Deering's John Deere Model R and JD Lanz D6516

DEERING'S DEERES

Chris McCullough finds a collector fascinated by John Deere

Ronnie Deering owns an impressive number of Lanz and McCormick tractors but the favourites in his collection carry the John Deere livery and his green collection is growing.

It already includes a nice 1969 John Deere 4020 with four-wheel drive and a 1949 Model R, but his latest restoration project is quite a rarity.

That tractor is a John Deere Lanz, which he says was built sometime in the 1960s. Because he was already interested in Lanz, Ronnie searched for a John Deere Lanz model and eventually found one in Western Australia of all places.

He recalled: "I wanted a model of a John Deere Lanz as I liked the concept and wanted this part of John Deere history in my collection. I tracked one down that was simply lying on a farm north of Perth and bought it from photos."

It took six weeks for the tractor to reach Ronnie's home at Newtownards in Northern Ireland almost two years ago but now the restoration is almost complete. His Lanz is the D6516 model, the biggest one made, and it is powered by a 65hp single-cylinder Lanz engine.

"It's a petrol-start diesel engine," explained Ronnie. "It was running well, although I did have to find a new injector nozzle in Holland. This particular model has a differential lock and creeper gears, although I don't understand why, as this is a hauling tractor with no hydraulic arms but with a pto system fitted."

And that hauling power was a problem for these tractors as, in a lot of cases, the front rims became fractured due to excessive power from this four-and-a-half ton beast.

Ronnie carried out most of the restoration himself, sourcing parts and tin work on the internet and from suppliers in Holland. However, when it came to spraying the tractor there was a problem.

"I went to one of the local paint suppliers with a part for them to colour-match. I duly sprayed the tractor and stood it in the yard when completed. My wife Margaret was walking past and told me it was the wrong colour. To my horror she was right. I am a little colour blind and never noticed this until it was too late, but thankfully the supplier changed the paint free of charge."

Ronnie fitted new tyres all round on the JD Lanz but had to go a long way to source the front ones. He said: "These are a 9.00 x 20 size and need to be a special strengthened version and the only place I could find these was in Russia. Covers

for the clutch and new side panels were sourced in Holland while most of the badging was sourced back in Australia."

The final piece of Ronnie's John Deere Lanz restoration project is to be a side seat, which he has decided to make himself once he obtains the correct photo of how it looked.

His John Deere Model R was also found in Western Australia in a place called Wyalkatchem. It was originally part of a Doe-style tractor conversion but was restored as one tractor. According to Ronnie it was in a very rough state when it arrived at his home but with tender, loving care has been restored to a very high standard.

However, his favourite John Deere tractor is his 1969 4020 model which he has owned for ten years.

He explained: "This six-cylinder model is rated around 100hp and I use it for light duties around the farm. It has Powershift, power steering and power brakes. It also has Power Front Wheel Drive operated by a hydraulic oil motor and engaged electronically from the dash. This system did create some problems when travelling down hills if four-wheel drive was engaged as the tractor could lose grip from the rear wheels.

"The 4020 is still my favourite. She is quite a unique model and creates a lot of attention at shows." ■

First Among Equals

The R featured several firsts and is still popular, says Peter Love

Ticking over on Tony Fisher's airstrip, the John Deere R has a unique sound to it.

It's been 60 years since John Deere's first diesel tractor, the R, hit the streets. It featured other 'firsts' and 21,293 models were sold; it's now become popular on the preservation scene.

In the mid-1930s John Deere saw a need to replace its biggest standard tractor, the D, because although it had been part of the company's success story since 1923 its power had reached its limits.

Deere had noted the success of Caterpillar and its fine diesel engines which were then powering most of its crawlers and the advantages of diesel over petrol/paraffin had become evident - excellent fuel efficiency, better power and torque curves, but above all lower costs.

When International Harvester Co came along with its diesel T-40 crawler in 1934 and its standard wheel WD-40 tractor a year later, John Deere really sat up and took notice.

It built two diesel versions of the D in 1938 and the tractors showed potential but, due to the two-cylinder horizontal configuration to which the company was totally committed, a completely new tractor design, top to bottom, was required.

Development continued with the experimental MX series that would eventually lead to the production R and by 1941 eight MX tractors were under field test. They featured an uncommonly high bonnet line, possibly because of the donkey starting engine being placed upright at the time.

In 1944 five more MX tractors came to fruition, now looking similar to how the final R was to look. In 1947 another eight were produced, this time with the two-cylinder opposed donkey starting engine that was to be the basis of what JD were to use on the R.

This last batch of experimental tractors was to be successful with one example logging some 4,000 hours while under test in Argentina.

As always the ultra-conservative John Deere company was very careful with its launch of the model R and it was introduced to dealers at Winnipeg, Manitoba, Canada, of all places, in June 1948. A few pre-production models were ready for the dealer's day and the men were mighty impressed with the final product. Many dealers went away knowing they had a winner to sell and a

The donkey engine is not hard to work on with the R and is well built.

The R's engine design is very neat.

superior product to the major opposition, the diesel McCormick-Deering WD-9.

The R was a very rugged tractor with a two-cylinder 416cu in 1,000rpm 5.75 x 8in bore and stroke engine (coincidently, that is the same bore and stroke as a Caterpillar D8).

To start the 16:1 compression ratio diesel engine a well-engineered and over-built 10hp opposed two-cylinder engine was fitted that ran at a sprightly

4,000rpm with Wico X magneto ignition and a six-volt electric starter.

The new diesel engine certainly packed a punch; under a rated load it could turn 43.52 on the belt and 34.45 on the drawbar. It was truly economic for its time and was capable of 17.35 horsepower hours per gallon: in other words it was a winner.

The first production example, number 1000, was sold to Louis Toavs of Wolf

Point, Montana, on March 1, 1949. He part-exchanged the tractor for an 80 model in 1955 but repurchased it in 1980 for his collection.

The standard transmission was a five-speed unit with a top speed of 11.5mph, but fourth was a low 5.5mph; if steel wheels were fitted then fifth was blocked out. However, a heavy-duty transmission was offered with different ratios and a top ➡

It was truly economic for its time and was capable of 17.35 horsepower hours per gallon: in other words it was a winner

The pto shaft is well hidden at the back and normally doesn't suffer from damage.

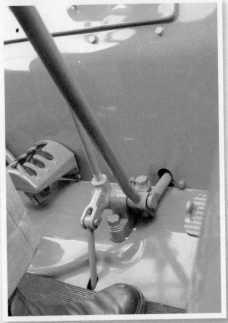

On all the lettered series range the clutch pivot pin normally needs replacing.

speed of only 5.5mph. The pto and hydraulics were optional equipment, but most came with these, or they were fitted at a later date.

By the end of production the tractor was down on power compared to its competitors in the high plains regions and prairies where it was used. In fact, 17,563 examples were sold to this area of the USA and Canada and the last to leave the Waterloo factory (on April 1, 1955) carried serial number 21863. The last home market example, however, number 22081, was made earlier on August 26, 1954, and that was sold to Memphis, Tennessee.

Today, many are still lying around the high plains area but a good number have been shipped to all parts of the globe for preservation, particularly to the UK and Republic of Ireland. The R has become a great collector's tractor.

AN OWNER'S VIEW

One person who has purchased a R model for restoration is Tony Fisher, who only likes the best and uses John Deeres on his extensive Cambridgeshire farm.

In between restoring and flying venerable Piper Cubs, Tony came across his ex-John Stephenson 1949 R at the Cheffins collective earlier this century. It was not the cheapest tractor to buy but, as a Lanz owner, he knew he had to have it.

The panels were so-so, although people had been walking on the bonnet, and something to consider with these tractors is that in many instances they won't have rusted owing to the area many of them worked in.

Most of the parts are available (at some cost) from your local John Deere dealer as well as the many parts suppliers that exist in the USA to service

SERIAL NUMBERS

1949	1000-2414	**1952**	9293-15092
1950	2415-6367	**1953**	15093-19092
1951	6368-9292	**1954**	19093-22293

They don't come up like this every day, but this example carries the large wheels and tyres and was sold at an HJ Pugh sale for £4,000.

JOHN DEERE DIESEL

Above: It's normal to need to replace the king pins on the R during the restoration as they are not over-large for such a big axle.

which are on a slight taper. Tony found the biggest puller he could and, with some oxygen and acetylene, the centre hub was warmed up and after a day's work they both eventually popped off. New front Goodyear tyres went on and the rears were half-useable so were left as they are.

The steering was totally overhauled, particularly the front axle with new king pins and bushes; the steering box was renovated.

Fitted with a new battery the tractor took some starting but, once you have got the knack, Tony says, she runs fine. You start the donkey engine and allow it to warm up, which in turn heats the diesel engine as the exhaust pre-warms the incoming intake air.

After leaving it to run for ten minutes or so Tony slowly pulls over the lever that engages the drive from the donkey engine to the main diesel engine and at the same time decompresses this engine.

After he has left the engines to turn over for some minutes the decompressor lever is disengaged before opening the throttle and, with any luck, he's away. However, if the weather turns cold it is not unknown for the cranking procedure to take 15 minutes before the tractor bursts into life and it's certainly advisable to have the diesel side of things and the donkey engine in first-class order or life can be rather frustrating.

Tony took the trouble to have the tractor sand-blasted and his staff repainted the tractor in two-pack after straightening the panels, particularly the bonnet, and fitting a new grille.

A new seat was installed and the job is now complete. Tony and his family enjoy the tractor to the full and he says it's very powerful and loves working on the threshing drum from morning till dusk, as well as baling jobs in the field.

The R was certainly a worthy replacement for the D, could hold its own against the opposition and nothing could beat it for fuel economy. ■

the extensive vintage JD range.

When Tony got the tractor home he stripped the engine down: the six-volt donkey engine starter was burnt out and a replacement was acquired, along with the main engine ring gear. However, the donkey engine itself was in excellent order and is classed by John Deere experts as far better than the later V-4 units that JD used on its numbered series of two-cylinder diesel tractors.

The main engine was stripped down, the bores were honed out and new piston rings were fitted. On went a set of big end shells and the oil pump was cleaned and tested and was found to be working well. The valve seats in the head were sorted out and new valves went in after the face of the head was cleaned and trued up. In fact, when you get down to it, the engine was in good order.

The individual diesel injector pumps were good, as were the injectors themselves – these are much easier to work on than later JD two-cylinder diesels. Obviously all the fuel and oil filters were renewed.

The water system was thoroughly tested and cleaned and a new fan belt was fitted. The hand clutch turned out to be in good order but the brake lining was renewed.

Lots of problems were encountered removing the rear 14x34.12 inch wheels

JOHN DEERE
Model "R"
DIESEL

THE COST-REDUCING TRACTOR
they're all talking about

THINKING OF BUYING ONE?

Tony says if you have a chance to hear the tractor run before buying it, do so. The parts are virtually all obtainable, but the cost can easily run away with you if you're not careful.

Good original examples can be found so do have a look at what is available on the market. What would you expect to pay for a running example that is straight? In the region of £3,000-£5,000.

Remember the tyres can be expensive to buy, particularly if the optional 26in wider rims and tyres are fitted, which certainly fill up the rear wheel arch!

Always check the steering, particularly the steering box, and of course the inherent weak point with these tractors – the pto drive gears, which require the transmission to be stripped right down if they need replacing.

Hi-Crop 60!

Peter Love takes a look at Tommy and Madeline Fennelly of Mad for Models fame very rare 1952 John Deere Hi-Crop 60H 6006064 that made its debut at the Fingal Rally, County Dublin on July 26-27 2008.

Hi-Crop 60

Hi-Crop tractors have a particular uniqueness about them and are valued extremely highly, particularly in North America. The only example in the United Kingdom and Republic of Ireland surfaced again on July 26-27 2008, after undergoing an 18 month re-restoration. Joint owner Tommy Fennelly takes time off from his Mad For Models stand to test the tractor out at the superb Fingal Vintage Society Ltd's super rally, at Rathmoony, Lusk, County Dublin.

I t was in 1997 that Tommy and Madeline first saw this tractor advertised in Tractor & Machinery. The couple just had to have the machine which was being offered on the market by that great building engineer Mike Thorne of the Coldridge Collection down in Devon. Mike houses a wonderful Ferguson – Massey Ferguson collection, even some still owned by AGCO.

This ex Florida 60H Hi-Crop is one of 62 straight petrol examples produced by JD between May 1952 (6000237) and July 1956 (6062736). The John Deere 60 Hi-Crop production was only 212, including 135 of the all-fuel version and 15 LP tractors. The total 60 production was a remarkable 61,105.

So why was the 60 so popular? Well for a start it was the replacement for the so successful model A row-crop. The 60 carried the 'new' modified engine with great affect. ➡

The dynamo can just be seen in front of the engine here.

Grandpa's little helper, Ned Tallon, tests the height of the 60.

Owing to the 180 degree firing order of the two-cylinder engine the single barrel carburettor did not necessarily supply the right hand cylinder the full amount of mixture required every time. It was always a compromise, but it worked, however the answer was a two barrel carburettor that Marvel-Schebler came up with, problem solved and the engine idle was vastly improved, it also gave the engine an extra 3.5 hp. However it is interesting to note that on the all-fuel model they reverted back to the single barrel carburettor.

Another area of improvement was the pto driven Power-Trol hydraulics, which was well liked by the industry. Also new on the 60 series was a governor hydraulic pump, which gave constant 'live' hydraulics. Using a similar system to the R pto that went 'live', the R system however ran on the flywheel side. This wasn't possible for the rowcrop numbered series so it was designed to take the engine power from the clutch side. In the first reduction cover an idler gear was placed with a set of reduction gears, in the backend a hydraulic pressure wet clutch

unit was placed with further reduction gears that gave the correct speed and direction, in fact the tractor produces 41.60 hp at the pto. The 60 also has a water pump fitted similar to the later A's, but this was further enhanced with an automatic temperature control with a bellows thermostat in place.

All these things the new owners of the only example Hi-Crop 60 at the time in Europe were to learn and for a number of years they rallied the tractor around in the Republic of Ireland. Eventually it became a little tired and was in need of a tidy up so it was taken off the road in 2007. The steering was totally rebushed including the king pins and centre pin, something that takes extra stress on a hi-crop compared to a row crop or standard model. The wheel bearings were also replaced, but the clutch disengagement had always been a problem. It was stripped to find the thrust fork end disintegrated, a new one was obtained from Kim Johnson in the USA, Kim has a photographic mind, just tell him the year and he knows the part number. All the panels were stripped back to bare metal and straightened out in

places, before red oxide was applied. New gauges were a feature here, besides a new wiring loom and the seat was sorted out.

With the engine in good condition it was time to paint the tractor in the correct JD colours using the two-pack paint system, remembering that the two-cylinder John Deeres are slightly dark in colour compared to the more classic examples. To finish it off the correct decals were applied something that was a little problem before this restoration. The tractor finally came together in June 2008 and made a triumphant return to the rally scene at the Fingal event at the end of July.

Having driven a similar 60 in Arizona a few years ago, I know the Hi-Crop has plenty of road speed. Tommy says it's a similar case and 25 mph plus is very caperable through the six-speed gearbox, he keeps at the back of the road runs not the front and just chugs along in fourth. Congratulations on the re-restoration of an old favourite and just like Mad For Models, another of the Fennelly's companies, it is nothing but the best and as Tommy says "From The Toy To The Real McCoy." ∎

Good progress is being made on the Hi-Crop 60 in 2007, have a close look at the way it is all laid out with Tommy and Madeline in November 2007.

You can clearly see the 'live' pto and the clutch mechanism on the rear end.

A beautifully-restored John Deere 620 Orchard seen in Canada. Photo: Peter Squires.

TWO-TONE DEBUT

Peter Squires takes a look at the successor to the John Deere 60

he Waterloo Iowa-built John Deere 620 was the successor to the Model 60 (1952-1956), which itself succeeded the model A.
Perhaps the biggest visible difference between the 60 and 620 was the new, two-tone green and yellow paintwork, even though the tin work is the same as the Model 60. The sheet metal was later redesigned for the 620's successor, the model 630.

A new "Float and Ride" seat was introduced on the JD 620 and the engine was completely redesigned to provide more horsepower. The price new in 1956 was $3,000 (about £1,600 at today's exchange rates).

A total of 22,600 JD 620s were built between 1956 and 1958 and they were available in four variants – the row crop 620, the standard 620S, the orchard 620-O, and the high-crop 620H.

The John Deere 630 was produced from 1958 to 1960 and replaced the 620, although the 620 orchard version (shown in the image above) continued to be produced after the standard model had been replaced (there being no 630 orchard derivative). For more 'Green' information have a look at www.retiredtractors.com and thanks also go to Harvey Hamilton for help with the John Deere 620 facts and specifications (visit: www.two-cylinder-restoration.com). ■

JOHN DEERE 620

Serial numbers:	1956: 6200000 1957: 6203778 1958: 6215048 Last serial no: 6223247		
Total built:	22,600		
Fuel:	Petrol, all-fuel, LP gas		
Cylinders:	2		
Bore/Stroke:	5.50x6.375in (140x162mm)		
Displacement:	302.9 ci (5.0L)		
Rated RPMs:	1125		
Horsepower:	Drawbar	pto/belt	
Petrol:	44.2	48.7	
Tractor fuel:	32.7	35.7	
LPG:	45.8	50.3	

Lynn's freshly-restored John Deere 530 gleams in the sunlight.

AN UGLY DUCKLING

Canadian reader Lynn Davies creates himself a swan

I have been an avid tractor collector for most of my 70 years and during that period I have collected and restored about 60 tractors, mainly John Deeres. This is the story of my entry for the "before and after ugly tractor contest."

My 1959 John Deere 530 row crop petrol model was shipped new from the JD factory to Portland, Oregon in the US. After that it came to Canada in the 1970s to a dairy farm in Abbotsford, British Columbia. It then went to North Central British Columbia to the logging/farm area of Prince George and it was there that I first saw this sorry hulk of what was once a beautiful tractor.

The owner was open to offers so I made one and the deal was on. I live in Sherwood Park, Alberta, and he delivered it to me and then I began a 100 per cent restoration.

The John Deere 30 line, built from 1958 to 1960, consisted of some of the finest

Lynn's John Deere 530 soon after it arrived in Alberta.

The adjustable front axle took some persuading to come apart.

The old pistons had definitely seen better days and so replacements went into the newly-honed bores.

tractors built anywhere. However, the lack of live pto, antiquated hand clutch and the need for great diesel power doomed them.

Today the JD 30 line is sought all over the world with the little 330 getting sale prices of over US$30,000. The JD 530 is hot on its heels at around US $20,000 to US $25,000.

My personal favourite is the JD 830 "Rice Special" electric start.

But back to my 530. When it arrived at my home its problems were:
- All four tyres flat, rear rims rusted out
- Engine stuck solid
- Both rear wheels stuck due to both brake drums being seized
- Stuck in gear due to sheared-off gear lever
- Showed signs of oil leaks from both rear axle seals
- Rear axle stuck solid due to condensation water freezing in housing
- Front axle adjustment stuck solid
- Power steering pump showing signs of generous leaks

The major missing parts were the nose cone, seat cage and battery box, muffler and pre-air cleaner, dash instruments, tachometer cable, rear mudguards and light and a large number of smaller parts.

The project was huge but not daunting as I had restored a 530 previously.

The first job was to make the tractor mobile and into the warmth of the workshop. I got air into the front tyres and removed the rims on the rear wheels; then I applied my Tiger Torch flamethrower on to the rear axle to melt the frozen ice and oil. I then drained it and towed/pushed/pulled/dragged it into the shop.

Once it was in the workshop I set about the seized motor and it was a big and ugly job to remove the connecting rods from the crankshaft. I sent the rods, blocks and pistons off to some engine rebuilders.

While the engine parts were away, I removed and renovated the brakes and drums, put new bushes and bearings into the starter and generator (and ordered a new wiring loom) and fixed new bearings and seals into the rear axle.

The next job was to steam-clean, blast and then prepare the steel for paint while sending off the sheet metal for priming and painting at a professional bodyshop.

I won't go into too much detail but by this point the other tasks I had completed included installing a new radiator core, starter, exhaust system, power steering hoses, all the electric gauges and the main rear axle bearings and seals.

New tyres and tubes were provided all round and I tracked down a nose cone to Kansas. I obtained all the other parts from Steiner or K&K, both in the USA.

The final big job was to free the front axle width adjustment.

To do this we found two large trees approximately 10 feet apart, two heavy logging chains, a large Tiger Torch flame thrower, a 30-ton "come along", a large sledgehammer, gallons of WD-40 breaking oil and allowed at least one or maybe two days to complete the job. It was worth it; the tractor now looks great!

The final step was to install the carburettor, plugs, and new leads, points, distributor cap, battery etc then the new battery box, seat, mudguards, lamps, bonnet, grille, change all the oils and anti-freeze and carefully install new clear decals. We turned the engine over for five minutes without the plug leads to lubricate and fill with petrol. So now, after 18 months, came the moment of truth.

Beautiful! It started on the first turn and the power steering, transmission, brakes, three-point hitch all worked perfectly. It was a great day with a great deal of personal satisfaction.

So what is my next project? I have yet another JD 530, a JD 60, a JD D and JD 820 rice special all lined up. ■

After blasting, the rolling chassis was treated to a coat of primer.

JOHN DEERE HEAVEN

We visit one of the worlds biggest collections of John Deere Tractors before the dispersal sale.
Fred Game reports

Little and large as the JD 9200 towers over the 1960s iconic 4020.

A lovely and rare 40 combine with a mighty 9750STS.

The Toavs family have finally decided to sell the collection.

The two-cylinder 840 scraper bowl with Hancock elevated scraper bowl behind, a well thought-of piece of kit.

You can only describe the Toavs family farm as in the middle of nowhere: it is actually some 15 miles north of Wolf Point, Montana, in the north-west of the USA.

Montana is not so far from Saskatchewan, just across the Canadian border, and it's 'big sky country.' It's big tractor country, too, and that's what the late Louis Alfred Toavs used on his farm which extended over many thousands of acres. You need that sort of acreage in these parts to obtain any decent kind of yield.

This is where he used no less than three mighty circa 1961 8010 artic tractors. They pulled 50ft grain drills very successfully but went back to the factory for transmission updates and came back as 8020s. Louis considered then dependable and fuel-efficient compared to other tractors of the time. His biggest regret was when he traded two of them in for a John Deere Wagner WA-14.

Louis Toavs was born on July 11, 1914, to Abraham F and Maria Michel Toavs in Ulen, Minnesota, the seventh of 15 children. He was two-years-old when he moved with his parents from Minnesota to a homestead north of Wolf Point, Montana.

Louis had a mechanical ear from an early age and during the 1930s worked at Camrud Motors, where he performed all manner of duties.

On June 3, 1937, he married Lena Koslowsky at Hawley, Minnesota. They moved to the farm on Tule Creek in 1939 and to the present farm in 1949, purchased from uncle NJ Toavs.

Louis developed the farm/ranch with great dedication and his cattle and arable crops increased. He loved each part of the seasons as he worked the land using modern John Deere equipment which he found very reliable, particularly in the face of JI Case which was popular in these parts with International not far behind.

Breaking up sod was one of his joys; he used horses in the early days, then the JD D followed by the lettered series and then the big John Deere four-wheel drives.

He lived life to the full and started collecting John Deere tractors when many were just giving them away. Being technically minded he knew what he was looking for and all about low serial numbers.

The collection includes a full set of Ds, one from every year of the 50-year production span, including one of the first 50 Ds fitted with the ladder side radiator and, of course, the 26 inch spoke flywheel that the first 879 carried.

The 8020 is just one of the 'New Generation' that is expected to make over £50,000.

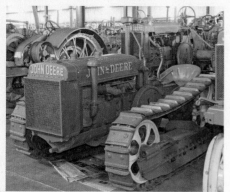

A rare a GPO-Linderman. Only 25 were built and half have lasted into preservation.

The GP tricycle, of which 72 were made in 1928-29.

Just part of the line-up of John Deere Ds with the very early ladder rack example closest to the camera.

This 'spoker' D does work and run by all accounts.

Although there is a similar collection in Canada, it is thought to be unique in the USA and a multitude of further rare types of D, like the orchard version, are included.

Not far away in Louis' museum building is an extremely rare and unsuccessful C, the forerunner to the GP.

Waterloo Boys will also be part of this sale, besides a Waterloo Boy tractor wheeled stationary engine unit of the same period.

Moving on in time, GP, GPO, AN, AW, BN, BW, and AR, again in a multitude of types and mostly rare, will come up.

Various types of Linderman crawlers are here from a D, to a GPO-L, BO-L AO-L, 62 and more.

Also stationed here is a very fine industrial line-up, including a mighty 1960 840 with Hancock self-lifting scraper bowl, 430 crawler with huge front blade, 430 forklift, AI, DI, 350 and more.

An astonishing number of lettered and number series tractors are also here from BW, BN, AW and AN right through to a 1949 R Diesel, said to be the first production model of this type.

Representative of the 1950s

are the low figure 50, 60, 70, 80 series moving on to the 830.

A good number of orchard tractors, or unusual types, are part of the collection and the dual John Deere with styled D on the front end which Louis actually used will certainly attract attention.

A number of the New Generation models are also included and combines are not forgotten and in varying conditions from a lovely 40 to a 42 and a 55.

There are more than 200 restored tractors on Louis' farm and about 300 unrestored - but weather is kinder to them there than it is in Britain.

Louis died on Christmas Day 2001, since then his daughter and the rest of the family have kept the collection going; a good number of visitors have made the long trek to view it.

As well as his tractors, Louis has amased a collection of some 2,000 models. It includes a large -scale 'spoker' D that actually runs and is exceedingly well-detailed, and other gems that cover a considerable period in John Deere model history: most are boxed. ■

John Deere junk heaven. All these items are related to the make in some way or another.

Rarely seen, a steel-wheeled model R. It's said that the first production R is in this collection.

German technology is part of the collection with the ex-Australian Lanz Bulldog 9500 series and 1960s John-Deere Lanz.

The replica of the John Deere forge and house is excellent and comes well recommended.

John Deere Heritage Tour

Today John Deere has become a major tourist attraction in all parts of the globe however the historic sites in the mid west of the USA are worth taking a look at. In recent times Peter and Jayne Love of P & J Tours have taken people to these sites and give us a brief look at what they are all about.

JOHN DEERE'S HOME Without doubt the historic John Deere home and forge at Grand Detour, Illinois a small town on the Rock River, is where you should start, some 100 miles from Chicago. Here there is a replica of that forge where he fashioned that famous plough and carried out repairs on farm equipment before concentrating on farm implements, not only ploughs, in those very early days. Demonstrations are given during the summer season by a blacksmith on making various items with the forge and a fascinating hour can be spent in this section alone. The house tour is excellent, particularly for the ladies, as we learn of the primitive air conditioning system John Deere created for his wife, three daughters and two sons who arrived here in early 1838. Before taking in the house the diorama with sound affects

This is an artist's impression of what the city of Mills; Moline looked like in the 1840's when the John Deere's plough works was set up.

This is just some of the 2009 international group that P & J Tours brought to the Pavilion. Our next visit will be in 2011.

Outside the Pavilion a good array of machinery is seen.

John Deere's very new visitors centre is excellent, as is the tour around the factory.

tells you the story of John Deere's parents Sara and William whose roots are based in Wales by all accounts. You need at least three hours to get the full flavour here at 8334 South Clinton Street, Grand Detour and to look at the land John Deere's plough was expected to plough through known as 'The Plough that Broke the Plains.'

JOHN DEERE HQ

Travelling some 90 miles south finds you in Moline, where the corporate headquarters are situated. Known

as the 'rusty palace' owing to the specially protected "environment steel" used in its construction, in 1,400 acres of lovely surroundings.

COMBINE FACTORY

Down at East Moline stands the famous John Deere combine factory. It's all that is left of this 'hub' of agriculture manufacturing as Moline was for so many companies. As one drives to the combine factory you pass the site of the former IHC combine works which was

situated right by the green works some ten years ago, but it's now just concrete. An excellent recently built visitor's centre greets you before you start your tour of this impressive modern factory.

JOHN DEERE PAVILION

After this it's off to downtown Moline and the impressive John Deere Pavilion at 1400 River Drive where you can see just some of John Deere's history, besides its current machinery placed around this site right by the Mississippi River. Next to the Pavilion is the John Deere store at 1300 River Drive where every kind of 'goody' can be bought even an Athern JD train set.

Just across the way, a 2009 painting by William Gustafson of what the site here looked like in the late 1847 with the Deere, Tate & Gould plough works, the feature certainly stands out on the side of the building. Sadly the John Deere Collectors Centre just down the road was closed in late 2008.

BUTTERWORTH CENTRE

Next on the list is the Butterworth Centre, which has two facilities in the form of the house of Charles Deere, John Deere's son, it's called Overlook. Charles continued the development of the company, and this house is set in seven acres high above the Mississippi River. Just a little further on is Charles Deere's daughter's house when she married William Butterworth set in three acres. These sites are on 1105-8th Street and 817-11th Street, Moline

To do all these things in a relaxed atmosphere will take you a good two days, but it is an education all in itself further details www.deere.com/en_US/attractions. The factory tour is not open to the general public as such and visits needs to be arranged through various parties. P & J Tours will be next visiting these sites on their 2011 Great American Shows Tour for further details, tel: 01323 833125. ■

All the latest technology goes into building a John Deere combine particularly in the paint process.

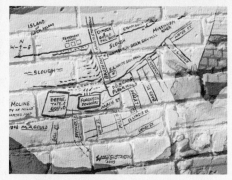

A close up of the road layout here, all part of William Gustafson's mural.

Seen in the John Deere Pavilion a replica of the very first plough.

The sight of seeing a 8010/20 is something very special.

The Revolutionary 'Eight-Ten' JD 8010/20

John Deere's artic was a revolution, but did it work?

As the 50th anniversary of the advanced John Deere 8010/20 artic tractor is upon us we take a look at this magnificent monster. At the time it was celebrated as the most powerful tractor offered by a mainstream tractor manufacturer.

The 'Eighty-Ten' as it was referred to in the trade, certainly got tongues wagging but it was to be a bit of a 'problem child' as time went on, as quite frankly it was underdeveloped. When you think about it, how did the ultra conservative Deere & Co ever come up with a tractor like this? To add to the situation the engineers were working hard on the new multi-cylinder five engine range and of course

NEW 4-wheel drive EIGHTY- TEN Diesel

... Remember— 5 full years of crops have been harvested with the tractors in this New Generation of Power!

Tested Power . . . . .

The brochure for the 8010 was very optimistic about what it could do.

The GM 6-71E could be an oily engine along the way with the supercharger seen here.

Spares for the GM engines are not hard to find in North America today.

'the New Generation of Power' tractors which were introduced at Deere Day in Dallas on 30th August 1960. These tractors were to eventually revolutionise tractor design and were an instant hit.

However, the 8010 story really starts in 1953. John Deere were looking to increase power, so they added a General Motors Detroit 4-71 to a Case 500 and when it was loaned to farmers they were very impressed with its power. However the engineers knew if four-wheel drive was to be added, more power would be needed to pull it through the ground. In fact it is said that JD field engineers attended the pioneering Steiger brothers' field day to see their machines at work and were seen taking notes and pictures.

What they come up with by 1959 was a 215hp monster with the use of the well proven GM Detroit two-stroke six-cylinder 6-71E engine. The 6-71 was a common feature in the truck and bus industry at the time. Deere & Co engineers coupled this to a 9-speed transmission, which gave a top speed of 18mph. For the axles the reliable Clark units were used, just the same as so many other dinosaur tractor manufactures had used over the decades, particularly in plant applications such as with Michigan. ➡

One of the experimental John Deere owned Case tractors that they tested with a General Motors Detroit 4-71 engine in1953. There is another example preserved in the Nebraska University's test facility museum today.

Seen in working order is this cabbed version of the mighty 8010/20.

You have plenty to press on the controls of the 8020, with the later eight-speed gearbox.

The tractor pivoted in the middle via its gudgeon pins, which let it rotate or twist by 16 degrees. It could even be used to operate safely on a 30 degree tilt. With the powerful steering hydraulic ram in full operation the 8010 could turn 17.5ft in a full radius. The air brakes fitted on all four wheels worked very well. The rear hydraulics offered no less than three 'live' circuits to the hydraulic couplings, but very few implements were available as such for a tractor like this, at least at the time it was made.

UK John Deere trooper Don Macmillan spoke to Tractor & Machinery about his September 1959 USA visit. It was to be the last great JD dealer's two-cylinder show, called the John Deere Field Day; it took place at Marshalltown, Iowa. In the tent was a pick-up F-180 eight-bottom plough and people were not quite sure what could pull such an implement. The 830, the largest two-cylinder of them all, was just a six-bottom plough tractor. Then low and behold and to the total amazement of everyone, a giant 215hp tractor of massive proportions appeared. It picked up the giant plough and in the afternoon was seen working and in action. Don says it was a moment in history that he will never forget.

The first production tractor 8010 left the line on 14th June 1960, but it would take some nine months to complete the 100 tractors and some were still in stock unsold in 1965, but the model was by then called the 8020 as we will see. When production started in 1960 the air cleaner was repositioned high in the air with a glass bowl on top and the headlights were now behind the grille and not in the header casting.

Unfortunately the Achilles heel of the tractor, at the beginning anyway, was the nine-speed transmission. It didn't like travelling at slow speeds with that eight-bottom plough behind and regularly blew apart. It couldn't breathe well enough, and the extra heat and slow speeds under load caused the adjoining fluid clutch/gearbox oil seal to blow, with dire affects to both departments. The answer was a stronger four-speed transmission with high and low range giving eight-speeds and a fluid pump equalizer to stop pressure building up in the hydraulic clutch and gearbox. Gone was the shift lever on the left side and it was now a floor mounted arrangement. It looks like in most cases the Dreyfuss Studio designed comfort seat, created with the help of orthopaedic

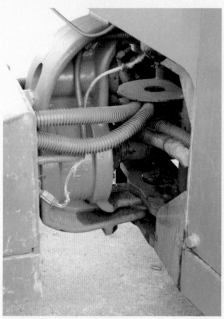

The pivot yoke on the 8010/20 with the inevitable oil leak.

It could almost be Marshalltown 1959, the weather is similar, but the tractor needs a polish.

Restored is this 8020, and with a cab at that, keeping everyone dry.

doctor Janet G Travell, was part of the new package. However I have seen a couple with the original flat seat along the way.

The factory took the brave decision to rebuild the tractors at their cost. Don Macmillan tells us that 1041 was the first to be rebuilt by the Waterloo factory in November 1963. This was certainly some time after the model had been introduced, but it was a slow seller and as we have seen, a number were still in stock some years later. However with a cost of just over $31,400 with a three-point hitch on the back it was a millionaire's tractor. For that money you could buy no less than four 80hp John Deere 4010s!

The rebuilt tractor was to be called the 8020 and it looks as though virtually all the original 100 that were built came back to the factory at some stage. Although it was very economic on fuel and environmentally friendly for its time, the 6-71E engine did not have the best power band. Unfortunately it lacked torque lowdown and you needed to rev the engine hard to get the best out of it and use the gears, but on some occasions the engine governor cut in early which didn't help. However they could pull 50ft grain drills all day when most farms could not cope with such equipment.

This side elevation of the 8020 clearly shows the comfort seat and the huge hydraulic levers.

Although John Deere promoted the tractor for industrial work it was not taken up by many. A number in preservation today show yellow paint underneath or even on top too, as was seen at the largest ever gathering of these 8020 tractors at the Half Century of Farm Progress, Rantoul, Illinois in late August 2009. John Deere certainly learnt a considerable amount in the field of artic tractors through the 8020, of which approximately half have lasted into preservation. Now that's saying something, but John Deere didn't get their artic sales right until the 7020 came along in 1971. ■

What a line up of these stunning machines that were ahead of their time.

The new silencer is fitted and painted in the correct matt black livery.

Yellow Power 1010

JD 1010 Industrial
Written by Peter Love

Well known Yorkshireman Henry Dixon a dairy farmer in Pembrokeshire started collecting vintage tractors years ago, but eventually decided to concentrate on one particular make, John Deere, and in particular the 10 series.

On 10th June 2005 our intrepid farmer flew into Chicago where he picked up a hire car and took his wife Margaret for a 16-day drive across North America. Besides sightseeing, his intention was to find a 10 or 20 series along the way. He had spoken to JD dealer Nick Dingler on the phone from the UK about some lift arms for his 4010 hi-crop. When Nick asked if there was anything else he could do for Henry, our keen collector explained what he was looking for. It just so happened that Nick had stored in a barn on a farm the very thing Henry was looking for, a 1962 1010 industrial gas. The tractor

The 1010 has just arrived at Kelch Restoration and Painting, Ohio, USA.

It's in quite a state as can be seen with the rusted out exhaust silencer, and rough grille, but essentially the panels are very straight.

Yes well it doesn't look that great, the throttle is on the left of the steering wheel. A new wheel was later acquired and fitted, the rest of the instruments were replaced, and the dash panel was to be straightened.

was said to run, but that was 20 years ago.

The deal was done in mid Ohio and after much discussion our Pembrokeshire collector decided to have it restored in the USA. For one thing it would be far better to obtain the parts in the 'fatherland' instead of constantly waiting for them to arrive here with all that that involves. However one thing worth remembering like most John Deeres nearly all the parts are available, and in this case 95 per cent, but at some cost.

Now who was recommended to restore this tractor for him? None other than Wendell Kelch from Bethel, Ohio, of 'Kelch's Restoration and Parts'. As Henry had bought the tractor as a runner, the first job for Wendell was to get it going and evaluate its condition. The tractor arrived with him in July 2006 and it was in quite a state when looked at closely. The Marvel-Schebler carburettor was chocked up and was replaced straight away. When it eventually fired up it smoked badly and it was in quite a state, it needed stripping down as there was water on the dip stick and that was for starters. This was not going to be cheap Henry!

There was nothing for it but to strip it all down and start again, off came the early front axle and the rest of the front end and then the engine, which was the first port

of call. This wasn't the best ever thing that Dubuque made, and after stripping off the cylinder head and sump it was pure water and rust that was found! Wendell says it was probably the anti-freeze that caused all the problems and created the corrosion in the first place as water passed down the side of the sleeves. It took quite something to lift the deck plate and sleeves up out of the block all as one and after some gentle tapping and lever bars each end, it lifted out and after the first inch it pulled out no problem. The block was crack tested and miraculously was in one piece; however a new camshaft was needed, besides the oil pump gears, big ends, main bearings and the camshaft timing gear.

The pistons were ok and the sleeves and deck remarkably good so could be used again. The sleeves were honed out and new rings were fitted to the pistons. The crankshaft was reground, and the whole engine was thoroughly pressure washed and degreased, which took some considerable time to do. It was reassembly time and it went together quite well. While this was going on a new manifold was being located and the dynamo and starter were being reconditioned. The cylinder head was skimmed, a must with these engines, and all the valves were replaced ➡

Now our engine is out and on end having been removed by the overhead crane, the filter gauze can clearly be seen.

Looking down from the top with all the selector rods removed, the rusty and chipped top gear in this five-speed box is clearly seen.

The engine is back in and everything is coming together it won't be long now. The front axle was also rebuilt, and new hubs were fitted.

Under test! The radiator has been cleaned and is under pressure test for water leaks.

Things were very worn on the JD PTO and had to be replaced.

Pushed outside and being run up, using the battery jump starter, all is well as the team look for leaks.

Those rear industrial Firestone tyres all on the rims however fitted so the paint touching up is done on the inside.

and reseated on the 36 bhp engine.

The gearbox was gone through and top gear was found to be chipped and worn so was replaced as were the bearings as necessary. The pto was in a mess; particularly the clutch plates and the pto input shaft had to be replaced as the splines were found to be displaced. All the ignition parts were replaced or overhauled; the distributor fits on top of the oil pump and was refreshed as they say. Over 45lbs of oil pressure was experienced on the gauge for the hour the engine was run up. The engine had previously been wire wheeled and etched painted in preparation for the rest of the restoration.

Now the overhead steering was overhauled, with new bearings and bushes on the shafts, as was the power steering hydraulic pump and valves. The next job was to stop all the hydraulic leaks remembering that the single hydraulics and pipes were now authentically piped in. This took

some time, especially the bending of the pipes, one had to step back to see if they were correctly positioned. Talking of the water hoses Wendell made sure he used the period clips which certainly look the part. Now with the tractor all mechanically sound, and no leaks whatsoever, it was off to Wendell's body shop, where his painter believes in nothing but cleanliness. The engine oil is then changed again to make sure no impurities are left in the engine.

The major replacement body wise was the battery tray and panel, which is quite complicated, it took his fabricator some time to do, but the end result is just spectacular. The grille was replaced with new, but the other panels were useable. They were bead blasted and a series of pictures was taken first to note the position of where the new decals were going to be placed on the tractor. These were going to be fitted after the PPG acrylic enamel John Deere industrial yellow (pre 1970 there is a

Wow the etched primer is all sprayed on and it will not be long before the filler primer is lightly sprayed.

The tractor is very complete with the linkage all fitted up and sprayed at the same time. The large spring under the hydraulic beam is expanded so that all the coils are painted inside.

It certainly is starting to look impressive and everyone is getting excited.

Coming together gradually, time and care was taken not to mark the paint and various areas are covered up in the process.

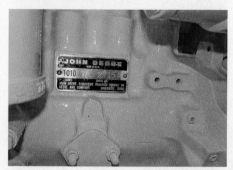

The authentic John Deere works plate of 1010, 27154.

What a lovely tractor seen in late spring 2007, with the new fuel cap in place and all painted.

difference) paint was hardened. Even the fuel tank was cleaned out properly and checked for leaks. Wendell tells me that if the fuel tank leaks, clean out with caloric acid which neutralises all the fuel vapour, he then solders and repairs the holes depending on what the age of the tank, is. To finish it off he places tank sealer fluid in the tank making sure it is covering the whole of the inside of the fuel tanks surface.

Now Wendell is not keen whatsoever on bead blasting the unit construction of the tractor, as the beads and sand get in everywhere and can cause and regularly do, irrevocable damage. He and his staff

use the 'whirly wheels' or 'buzzer cookies, as the Americans call them. They shine the metal up like new, but the job needs to be done properly in a warm environment. After cleaning the assembly off, PPG etched primer (matt black) is sprayed on in the heated oven and left to dry.

All in all three coats of PPG fibre filler are sprayed onto the paintwork and rubbed down as required with 400-800 grit paper, that's after the last coat. As with North American tractors the panels are 'glass' finish, but the unit construction is kept as it was when it came out the factory as just a rough casting and not filled as we tend to

Two 7hp compressors are kept in the little shed to the side of our picture, as the 1948 Willys CJ2A sits at the back of the 1010.

do. This is the way I personally like to see a tractor as it looks more realistic. The top coat is applied 'wet on wet' and left to dry in the heated oven, which bakes the paint hard, but flexible, that is why Wendell's team like using it. Obviously all the panels are sprayed off the tractor and then assembled after the basic unit is finished. All in all each item has eight coats of paint sprayed on it.

The Firestone industrial rear 12-28s tyres and tubes are fitted to the wheels backwards so if any touching up needs to be done it will be on the inside of the rim not the outside where you will see it.

In May of 2007 it was wrapped up in a plastic cocoon before being picked up. A little time passed before the 1010 was taken up into Canada by Antrac Services and loaded to Liverpool, from where it was shipped to Wales, some 30 miles from Henry's home.

It was an exciting time from Henry and Margaret and at all stages Wendell kept them informed of progress and sent pictures so they knew what to expect. The culmination of Wendell's Kelch's team's hard work came when the tractor was to win at the Scottish National show in September 2009 and it has picked up other awards at various shows as well. ■

Even the rear light is in the correct position and has always lived on the tractor since it was built in 1962.

Leaping Ahead

Scott Lambert profiles a Sixties pocket rocket

This early example of a John Deere 1020 was imported from Arnhem in the Netherlands by Nick Young and is now owned by Ivan Barrett of Cambridgeshire. It is used at local ploughing matches with a Ransomes two-furrow plough and is seen here at Ramsey Rural Museum's 2007 plough day.

T he John Deere 1020 is one of those tractors that leaves you with a smile on your face – for the way it looks, sounds and, more importantly, the way it performs. It may not have the long-stroke characteristics of a McCormick IH 523 or the sturdy feel of a Nuffield 10/42, but it'll make you wonder why John Deere never sold more.

DOMINANT FORCE
Back in the 1960s, John Deere was finding its feet in the murky waters of UK agricultural machinery sales and finding it hard to build up the reputation enjoyed by the long-running British marques – but that doesn't mean to say that its products weren't good. For farmers it was that old case of 'stick with what you know' as they could trace the lineage of a Coventry-built MF 135, but couldn't be sure how John Deere's multi-cylinder tractors had come about.

Model As, and the like, had appeared in Britain as part of the Lend-Lease agreement during the war years, but these 'Johnny Poppers' were poles apart from the multi-cylinder units that were now all the rage and, as such, could scarcely bear comparison. It was also difficult for farmers to comprehend the pedigree of the 1020 and its siblings when they heard that they were built in the same factory as the Lanz Bulldog.

At this point, it is worth mentioning that the 1020 was aimed squarely at the global agricultural community, not just Europe, with petrol and diesel variants being produced in Dubuque, Iowa and Mexico – as well as the tractors built for the European market in Mannheim.

It's also worth remembering that John Deere wouldn't be the dominant force that it is today without the models that built up a loyal following in the 1960s and '70s. It's tractors like the 1020 that helped pave the way for the market share enjoyed by the 50 Series and 6000 Series – tractors that were built with everyday use in mind – solid, reliable and ergonomically superior to many of the other tractors on the market at the time.

PERKINS' RIVAL
At the heart of any great tractor is the engine and in this case it was an in-house three-cylinder diesel that was chosen to provide the power. A petrol version was available, but this was predominantly seen in the Americas where fuel prices were lower and much less of a concern to farmers.

The French-built JD 152D powerplant had remarkably similar characteristics to the Perkins AD3.152 unit used in the Massey Ferguson 135 – with the same displacement, identical bore and stroke dimensions and very similar horsepower and torque figures. This was, of course, no bad thing! Perhaps it was an intentional decision by Deere to build the engine to an almost identical ➡

The first incarnation of the John Deere 152D three-cylinder engine, as fitted to this tractor, produced 44hp, while later models were equipped with a 47hp version.

specification to the Perkins unit as this would give salesmen a fighting chance of scoring a sale over the popular 135.

Upon its launch in 1965 the 1020 was powered by a 44hp version of the 152D engine, complete with a Roto-Diesel fuel injection pump – built under licence from CAV – and Roosa-Master pencil-type injectors, but this ensemble was eventually updated so that tractors sold in the latter months of 1971 were producing a useful 47hp. Irrespective of power, the engine had good torque and pulled well, with a lovely three-cylinder exhaust note thundering from the black, oval-shaped silencer.

for every eventuality
Like the vast majority of tractors on the market at the time, the 1020 featured a constant-mesh transmission that had eight forward speeds and four reverse, via a dual-range system. This was more than adequate for most farmers, but for those looking for a change-on-the-move facility, Deere's optional high-low gearbox doubled the number of gears available to the operator. This was much like any other 'splitter' of the time and provided a clutchless change that was perfect when ploughing in tough ground or getting up to speed on the road. The range of speeds available was good, with a speed of 1.3mph achieved in first gear and a useful road speed of 15.1mph on-hand for transport operations.

The tractor shown in the photographs is not fitted with a handbrake and uses the park position on the range selection lever to stop it from freewheeling – much like the high-horsepower Deeres of today. A traditional handbrake appears to have been an option, but few tractors seem to have been fitted with one.

The 1020 was equipped with either a dual-stage clutch or an independent pto

system. The dual clutch was much the same as those produced by other tractor manufacturers, but the independent pto was streets ahead of the opposition. It was actuated by a lever positioned between the two gear levers and was feather-light in operation – a truly unique selling point. Incidentally, one of the most obvious differences between the little Deere and those used to driving a Massey Ferguson was that the gear levers were the opposite way round, with the range lever on the left-hand side.

A 540rpm pto was standard equipment, but an optional 540/1,000rpm unit added an extra dimension. Scarcely seen in Britain, but more common on Continental farms was the 1,000rpm front pto option. This was specified in the main by livestock farmers who used their 1020 for cutting hay; it was perfect for allowing the use of a mid-mounted mower.

ADVANCED HYDRAULICS
The little Deere's engine and transmission were good, but the hydraulic system was in a league of its own. International Harvester's Vary Touch system, featured on the 434, and the Ferguson system fitted to the MF 135 were both very good –but John Deere opted to move away from traditional top-link-sensed hydraulics.

The closed-centre system employed in the 1020 was unique for a tractor in this horsepower range, in that it was lower-link sensed. At the time, John Deere was one of the pioneers of such systems, although other manufacturers had utilised similar set-ups on bigger tractors. In 1968, IH for example, would employ lower-link sensing on the 634, but this was a tractor in the 60-70hp bracket and markedly different to the 1020. The beauty of lower-link sensing is that

it acts so quickly and the 1020 certainly proved this when ploughing. When significant resistance was encountered, the force acted through the lower links on to the flexible torsion bar housed inside the back-end and via a series of linkages to the hydraulic piston – which then raised the implement automatically. With a constant and precise raising and lowering of the implement at a significant speed, the operator had the faith to snatch another gear – increasing output on primary tillage jobs.

Many farmers believed that this type of system was only really appropriate for high-horsepower tractors operating heavy-draft and semi-mounted implements. Those that bought the 1020 quickly realised that was not the case, but many were still sceptical about the merits of such hydraulics and steered well clear of the tractor – opting for those with the tried and tested top-link-sensed system instead.

An interesting system dubbed 'selective hitch control' enabled the operator to switch between position and draft control at either end of the scale and what was effectively a blend of the two in between. This controlled the dual-category linkage which had a lift capacity of 1,043kg (2,300lbs).

FIT FOR A KING
The Seventies was the decade that saw major changes in operator safety and comfort with the advent of safety cabs,

JOHN DEERE 1020: FAV 212C

The tractor featured here is an early example of a 1020 and is owned by Ivan Barrett of Cambridgeshire.

Having worked for local Ford agent, Gravens, Ivan was keen to find a New Performance Super Dexta to pull his father's Ransomes two-furrow plough, but was made aware of this particular tractor in the yard of John Deere specialist, Nick Young. A brief spell at Deere agent, Peter Hitchcock, in the early 1970s was enough to convince Ivan that the 1020 was the right tractor to buy and that the search for a Super Dexta should go on hold.

Nick had imported the tractor from Arnhem in the Netherlands and as such, it was equipped with continental-style mudguards – which Ivan changed to the British-style units.

Ivan is very complimentary about the 1020 and says it is the ideal tractor for him, with its excellent engine, hydraulics and ergonomics combining to make it an excellent ploughing machine.

Ivan is keen to learn more about the history of his tractor and is appealing to T&M readers to provide any information they can. The tractor carries serial number 045804L and engine number 063425CD.

PRICES

Rough, off-farm:	£750-£1,500
Good, off-farm/ excellent original:	£1,500-£2,500
Well-restored:	£2,500-£3,500
Concours:	£4,000-£5,000
	(Prices are approximate)

but in the 1960s tractor manufacturers had begun to comprehend that the more comfortable a tractor was, the more hours the driver would spend in the seat. The more productive the tractor was, the more likely the farmer would be to buy another of the same brand.

John Deere had been quick to realise this and set about placing almost as much emphasis on the operator's platform as it did on the mechanical side of its tractors. The 1020 featured a fully-padded seat, with shock absorber, that was adjustable to the driver's height and weight.

The hand throttle, hydraulic quadrant and pedals were all within easy reach and, critically, the gear levers were at hand (while being far enough away from the seat to allow your foot to pass by when disembarking) and a foot throttle was standard and was positioned above the right-hand footplate, attached to the bell-

housing – a much better position than the optional control on the MF 135. It is clear that a lot of thought went in to designing the operator environment as, even today, the 1020 is a pleasant tractor to operate for any length of time, irrespective of the job being undertaken.

OPTIONAL EXTRAS

During the late-1960s the retro-fit cab was a common sight on tractors of all makes and models and the John Deere 1020 was no exception. In Europe the iconic Fritzmeier cab, with its flip-up windscreen, was popular – but British farmers chose either Lambourn or Duncan units to adorn their tractor. Neither was particularly attractive or u luxurious, but kept the wind and rain at bay and helped to retain a bit of heat from the transmission in the winter months.

Additional ballast was available in the form of wheel weights, but front-mounted

slab-style weights were the popular choice for those wanting a bit of extra nose weight. These were the bolt-on type more commonly seen on the bigger, American-built tractors such as the 4020.

The 1020 looked a little on the small side to be a materials handler, but some farmers opted to fit a loader to their tractor. MIL loaders were a common fitment, possibly due to their complementary colour scheme, but other marques were also prevalent.

Standard tyre equipment on the 1020 was 6.00x16 on the front and 11x28 on the rear, although 11x36 tyres were available as an option.

BUILDING ON SUCCESS

Although the 1020 would never set the farming world alight, it proved to be reliable and a technological success – particularly in terms of the lower-link-sensed hydraulic system. After a demonstration, most ➠

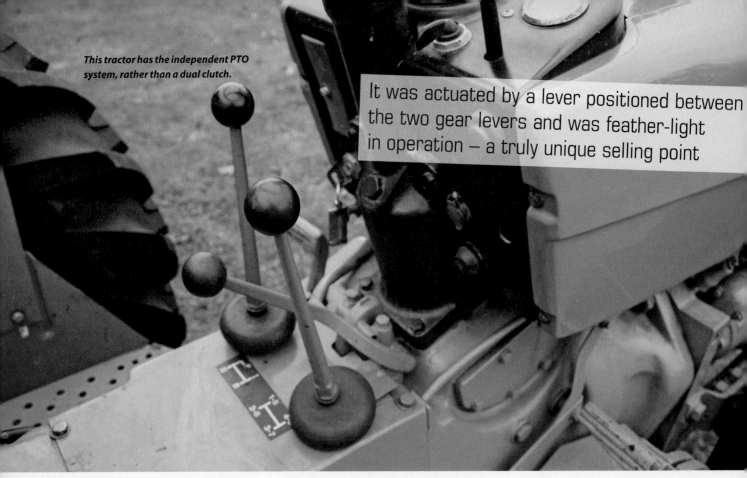

This tractor has the independent PTO system, rather than a dual clutch.

It was actuated by a lever positioned between the two gear levers and was feather-light in operation – a truly unique selling point

farmers were sold on the 1020's capabilities, but some shunned the tractor because John Deere was still a lesser-known manufacturer in terms of its multi-cylinder machines.

It was to be some years before John Deere would become a significant force in agricultural machinery sales and this was, in part, due to the high-quality tractors it had built in the 1960s and '70s – a stepping-stone to the market domination it currently enjoys.

Tractors like the 1020 are becoming increasingly popular with enthusiasts today because of the supremacy of the brand in current agricultural practice – with more and more appearing at rallies and ploughing matches up and down the country.

Due to the 1020 being a more popular tractor in mainland Europe than it was in Britain, most collectors are finding that it is often more viable to import one from abroad and take advantage of the

comprehensive parts availability in the UK, should they require it. Because of its useful size, horsepower and commendable German build quality, the 1020 and its siblings are likely to remain popular with enthusiasts – small consolation perhaps that it never made more of a mark in Britain on its release. ∎

The striking colour scheme, 'horseshoe' bonnet and attractive detailing make it hard not to like the John Deere 1020.

JOHN DEERE 1020

Engine:	John Deere 152D
Engine power:	44hp ('65 -'71) 47hp ('71 - '74)
Rated speed:	2,500 rpm
Max torque (Nm):	109.2lb /148ft @1,500 rpm
Cylinders:	3
Displacement:	152 cu in / 2,490 cc
Bore:	3.86in / 98mm
Stroke:	4.33in / 110mm
Fuel Tank:	13.8 gal / 62.5lt
Transmission:	8Fx4R (optional 16Fx8R)
Linkage:	Category I & II
Lift capacity:	2,300lb / 1,043kg
Turning radius:	259.8in / 6,600mm
Length:	135in / 3,430mm
Tread width:	53.1-76.7in / 1,350-1,950mm
Weight:	4,099lb / 1,859kg
Tyre size (front):	6.00x16
Tyre size (rear):	11x28 (11x36 optional)

3020 Classic Green Line

Seen in Wisconsin, USA at the Walter Keller and son magnificent John Deere collection is the 22nd September 1964 3020 LPG orchard serial number 181R069189. It was supplied to Winterhaven, Florida to work in the orchards in the area. There were nine 3020 gas orchards made by the company, but no LPG orchard versions whatsoever. However three retro fitted examples are listed by the Waterloo factory sold to Florida and this is one of the three. The fuel tank used was from the 3010 model and fits snugly under the tin work. As with LPG tractors the engine runs very smoothly, but of course is not so powerful on LPG. We thank the Keller's for bringing the tractor out for photographing. **Photo: Peter Love.**

More of these types of tractors are coming up and selling well at auction and Nick Young Tractors has the parts available to restore them.

JD 20 Series 'Kings'

Peter Love takes a look at Nick Young Tractors who are known as the '20 Series Kings'

O ne company who has done so much to put the 'New Generation' on the map for collectors and current users of these machines is Nick Young Tractors near Holton-Le-Moore, Lincolnshire. He very much specialises in the Mannheim built 20 range, which came on line from 1967 in Europe.

Today people come from all across Europe especially to use his services whether they require spares, engine rebuilds, cabs, restored tractors or second hand tractors Nick Young and his family are the people to see, without doubt the first port of call.

Nick has been cloned' in the green from an early age and went off to be a tutor at Nottinghamshire College of Agriculture before finding things rather frustrating and moved on to Holton Tractors where he created a second hand parts business for the company. However it was time for him to go it on his own in 1996 and so he set up at his current base and has been going strong some 14 years.

Seen checking out an early 3130 is Nick Young who keeps plenty of parts for these tractors.

Nick and James Young with one of their tractors that the mechanical work has been carried out on.

Their stand holds lots of parts for all kinds of 'New Generation' tractors, particularly those made at Mannheim.

Parts for the smaller 30 series are also available and were supplied for this restoration.

A wonderful 3120 that came Nick's way and is now in preservation.

The early 1630 was sold to Northern Ireland later in the day from this show and was a stunning restoration.

Customers followed him, particularly on the green side, as he had the knowledge of where to find the parts for the older tractors from the 40 series downwards.

Many requests were received for glass and cab panels, particularly on the OPU cab (Operators Protective Unit). However this was just the start of it as people phoned him up from all over Europe, particularly as they got to know him and what he was about and he also developed his own lines on various parts as well.

However it was the 20 series that has established as the 'man of all seasons' as apart from his knowledge and skill on the subject he has the goods at hand and also has a raft of these very reliable tractors in stock.

When they first came on the scene over 40 years ago the smaller 20 Series had problems and has what was known as 'dirty' diesel engine, but technology has changed and with later new liners, pistons and seals that can be fitted to the earlier blocks and various other refinements the engine can be transformed into a winner, which the later three-cylinder engines were. In fact with a 20 series you get a more powerful tractor than the Massey Ferguson 135 and one that

is very economic with the fuel. The hydraulic sensing arms leaked on the shaft arms, but a new neoprene seal has been developed and, as long as the shaft is not pitted, for just £10 and a couple of hours work the problem can be solved.

At present the company has a 1020 under restoration, which is due to be finished in a short while and is similar to the example that Scott Lambert tested (see page 52 of the book) so do give them a ring, it carries a warranty as well. Another economy tractor that makes it ideal for road runs and small holdings is the 920 40hp that came along in 1967, besides the 820 and 1120. The later was known as the 1520 in North America. Again these three-cylinder products are a good bet and are going up in value and not down.

The earlier New Generation from Dubuque, particularly the 1010 and 1020, Nick advises are not really for beginners. With their fixed liners and plate all in one they need some handling to get right (see page 48 of the book) but can be tackled if required.

The North American 20 series that came to the UK is also looked after by Nick from the 3020 and 4020 where wings and lights for European specification machines are all catered for.

Moving on the 30 series, these are becoming more popular as time goes on and the smaller examples like the 1630 that came along in 1973 can be a good bet. Many were used as yard scrapers and have also been exported, that applies to the Generation II tractors that came in 1975 too. However the older style six-cylinder 3130 is also sought after and that applies to the 3120, Mannheim's first six-cylinder too. The engine needs a good overhaul after 3500 hours or so on these, but generally they are reliable performers.

However the 20 series is certainly the favourite and is an ideal way into preservation, so what does a fully restored example cost, that's to a very high standard, well around £7,500 and examples waiting restoration or in good running order start at £3,000 upwards. For further details do give Nick Young Tractors a ring, whether it's for spares or a tractor, tel: 01673 828883 or do visit: www.nytractorparts.co.uk ■

Looking superb is this 1020 all gleaming and ready to go for a future in preservation.

JOHN DEERE 4020

Dave's JD 4020 was completely restored to a high standard, before he bought it, to celebrate 25 years of Powershift transmissions in the UK.

The Powershift Deeres of the late 1960s are rare in the UK, especially the original British-supplied models but Howard Sherren finds a spectacular example

It was in contracting that the 4020 covered more than 10,000 acres of ploughing, followed by as much as 1,000 acres of drilling per year

hen John Deere's 4020 was launched, it was a monster compared to its contemporaries: it boasted 100 horses under the bonnet.

At the time, farmers were after greater power to carry out operations more quickly and efficiently and hooking multiple implements or wider machinery to the back of these big tractors gave arable farms a completely new work rate.

As part of the "Long Green Line" the 4020 was an impressive beast - not only did it have incredible power from a diesel engine but it also had a full Powershift transmission, unlike the competition.

Some farmers were sceptical about this new design at first, but the tractor's reliability built a reputation for which the company is still famous.

The 4020 diesel first became available in 1964 when it was sold in the US alongside the petrol and LP gas models. It was only the diesel model that was brought into Britain – and sadly only sold in small numbers mainly due to the massive price tag.

One of these models now belongs to Dave Harrison of Hale, Merseyside, and it has seen a massive amount of action in its 45-year life. With 19,000 hours on the clock, the tractor is still in remarkable condition.

It was sold new to agricultural contractor Parson Brothers in Gloucestershire in 1965 where it was the prime mover and clocked up an impressive 7,400 hours.

It was in contracting that the 4020 covered more than 10,000 acres of ploughing, followed by as much as 1,000 acres of drilling per year. In addition it was responsible for spreading 10,000 loads of manure and many hours of front loader work.

Surprisingly, it also found its home on the silage clamp buck raking and produced over a million bales in its working life. For this, the 4020 became famous and was seen in the Guinness Book of Records in addition to the John Deere fact book.

Admittedly, the tractor hasn't got to these colossal hours without a bit of work and spannering – as much as John Deere would have liked it to.

It is believed that the tractor had two engine rebuilds to keep it pumping out the horses but it is claimed still to have the original crankshaft in it, which amazingly hasn't been reground. When the tractor was hooked to a dynamometer in 1989, it pushed out a massive 107hp at the shaft, which equates to at least 120hp at the flywheel.

The electrics became problematic as wires became brittle and connections corroded with use and weathering; which is why it has received two electrical overhauls over the years, as well as hydraulic pump work.

After 24 years of sterling service the tractor was treated to a full cosmetic refurbishment to commemorate 25 years of John Deere Powershift transmissions being in the United Kingdom. ➡

Designed for pulling, the link arms don't look up to the job.

Impressively, even after its 19,000 hours of use the gearbox hadn't been touched – and that number of hours equates to a car travelling over 950,000 miles!

The tractor was added to Dave's collection in 1989 and has always been a talking point among visitors and show-goers.

It recently took part in the Three Coasts annual vintage charity road run. Spanning six days and 550 miles, a group of tractors travel from Liverpool to Whitby and back, an impressive drive and an event many of the participants look forward to every year.

FORTY TWENTY DEVELOPMENT

The Waterloo-built 4020 originates from the early 1950s when development of a new line of high-powered tractors started. After seven years of work the 4010 was revealed and its host of new features immediately worried the opposition.

A few complaints arose that the 4010 didn't have the same fuel economy as the existing, smaller 730 and others commented on the lack of the power compared to the 830.

Deere decided to improve both with the release of the 4020, which was now fitted with a Powershift transmission to compete with the likes of Ford's Select-O-Speed gearboxes, among others, which seemed to be coming into fashion in the early 1960s.

The new box was no way a torque amplifier, which many were, and, unlike the competition, was controlled by just one lever. With this single control, eight forward speeds could be selected easily, with range levers and clutch pedals banished. The clutch pedal became an inching pedal for attaching machinery and, with plenty of horses under the bonnet, the eight gears in well-spaced ranges were found adequate - especially when changes up and down could be made on the move. Also, going from forward to any of the four reverse gears was completely clutchless.

For those who wanted a more traditional

The 4020's instrument panel with Powershift lever to the right of the steering wheel and hydraulic controls to the left.

change, the Synchro-Range transmission was still available at a reduced cost, but was improved in places to handle the extra power of this updated model.

BIG SPECIFICATION

The six-cylinder lump in the 4020 was your typical wet sleeve unit with 6,600cc from a 108mm bore and longer than average 121mm stroke.

Producing the maximum power of 100hp at 2,200rpm, the maximum transport speed was 2,500rpm and equated to just over 20mph on the road.

The closed centre hydraulics provided 2250psi at 49.2 litres a minute and had a capacity of just over 45 litres – a very good output for the period.

The linkage managed 1,719kg lift and had both 540rpm and 1000rpm pto speeds.

An additional feature from 1965 that the 4020 carried over other models was a diff-lock operated by the driver's right heel.

The 4020 wasn't too dissimilar in styling to the earlier 4010 apart from a new concave dashboard and new-look rpm gauge and hour meter. The Powershift models also benefited from a transmission oil pressure light and temperature gauge in addition to the fuel and temperature gauge.

The standard electrical system was 12-volt, provided by special long batteries, and used a positive earth until 1969 when it changed to the more standard negative type. The rear mudguards were changed to house headlights in the front to match the larger 5010.

With production peaking at up to 75 tractors a day, the 4020 was in demand through the late Sixties but production ended in 1972.

The few 4020s that made it to Britain are a good indication of the build quality and over-engineered design of many of the early models of John Deere tractors. ∎

Serial numbers

Year	From	To
1964	65000	90999
1965	91000	118999
1966	119000	145659
1967	145660	173981
1968	173982	200999
1969	201000	222159
1970	222160	249999
1971	250000	260790
1972	260791	
Last	270288	

JOHN DEERE 4020

Engine make:	John Deere
Max engine power:	100 hp
Max power @ (rpm):	2,500
Max torque:	353 Nm
Max torque @ (rpm):	1,100
Number of cylinders:	6
Displacement:	6,600 cc
Bore:	108 mm
Stroke:	121 mm
Fuel tank capacity:	128 litres
Top speed:	20.5 mph
Standard transmission:	8F x4R (Powershift)
Turning radius:	3,300 mm
Length:	3,830 mm
Width:	2,270 mm
Standard weight:	4,336 kg
Std. tyre size, front:	7.50-18
Std. tyre size, back:	18.4 R34
Cab:	N/A
Production from:	1964
Production to:	1972

The 4020 with its Powershift transmission has been a testament to the reliability of John Deere's transmission.

Giant of the Field

Peter Love looks at a just refurbished John Deere 5020 that has lived in the United Kingdom all its life. At one time the 5020 was the most powerful two-wheel drive tractor in the world and was certainly the 'Giant of the Field' during the 1960s.

'Power to the people' that's what Tony Macer says, this was the most powerful two-wheel tractor at the time of manufacture.

T he 'New Generation' of John Deere got going in 1960, but the biggest to join the 10 series was the 5010, which left Waterloo two years later than the others, in 1962. It was certainly the largest conventional tractor the company had built. In fact John Deere converted a Case LA with a 108hp GM 2-stroke engine and tested it in a remote High Plains location and the engineer's thought a high horsepower machine could be useful for the high grain acreage farmer. Back at their Waterloo base in 1953 they thought of a 100hp V-8 or V-6 unit which would certainly suit the salesman who were looking to the future, not forgetting this was the pre turbocharger era. However minds were made up in 1958 and John Deere decided to go for in-line cylinder power and for the largest in the line they came up with a six-cylinder 531 cubic inch (8.698cc) engine. The six-cylinder engine had a 4.75 x 5 inch bore and stroke with a 16-1 compression ratio and was a wet-sleeve engine; it would serve the company well as there was lots of development on it over the years. Called the variable speed engine it was fully governed to run between 600 and 2500 rpm. The full pressure lubrication had by-pass cooling, the seven-bearing crank was a feature and the injection equipment featured a rotary DPA pump.

Keeping things in the family has always been John Deere's policy and they used a transmission similar to that which was used in the most popular of the range the iconic 4010 and 3010; however it was much more beefed up for the extra hp, and stood the test of time competently. The 8-speed shuttle-shift Syncro-Range box offered 'on the go' changing, which could cause some problems if not handled properly, but gave a good range of speeds up to 20mph. Basically it offered four main ratios with high and low in each gear and the three lowest gears had reverse which was very handy for certain jobs around the farm or on industrial applications where this tractor became very popular at one time.

When tested at Nebraska in the summer of 1962 the 5010 produced 108.91dbh, the first tractor ever tested that produced over 100dbh. The hydraulically operated PTO produced a remarkable 121.12 hp. It could have been ready earlier, but John Deere wanted to get mileage on the 'Giant of the Field' and have it right from the off. With this in mind tests in the south took place, in the Arkansas rice fields and in the North West up in Oregon and Washington State. This all certainly helped the tractor along and the linkage was redesigned at this stage to make it even stronger. The massive planetary final drives certainly came into their own working in these areas of the USA, the tractor started strong and just got stronger over the years.

On the 3010 and 4010 the PTO was offered in two speeds, but on the 5010 that wasn't to be the case. Owing to ASAE standards, the engineers went for only one setting at ➡

The next project to be undertaken by Tony Macer and Maurice Houghton, is the unstyled John Deere A rowcrop which Nigel Burgess has got well on its way.

That heavy duty axle can clearly be seen in our picture and the wonderful clear lines of the Drafuss Studio styling.

Those clamshell wings hide the width of those rear tyres very well.

1000rpm, which suited it well. There has been a distinct family resemblance with all of the John Deere range from time memorial and that was again the case here. Style designer Dreyfuss did a good job, as he did on the 'Personal-Posture' seat which comes into its own with these mighty tractors and the frontage on the 5010/20 huge. It hides the 48 American gallon fuel tank placed at the front which certainly took some filling, as they were quite thirsty machines at the time.

The full wings were standard throughout the 50 series and a range of good lighting was provided in them as well, being neatly positioned under the front wing lip. Hydraulics played a major part in this monster and the high velocity pump provided supply and power to the brakes, steering, PTO, linkage and the remote

external cylinders which controlled the front steering wheels. These replaced the steering motor that was used on the small but more popular 3010 and 4010.

Interestingly a new larger rear sized tyre had to be developed especially for the 5010 by Goodyear and Firestone, 24.5 x 32 inch, this was to become a popular combine size eventually. Even dual wheels were a feature on these tractors, but narrower and a slightly different size. Category three/two linkage with Quik-Coupler was another first for any tractor at the time. Also a number of special implements were specifically designed for these machines, something that was a failure particularly when thinking about the Marshall MP6 and David Brown 50D. The 5010/20 was capable of safely handling a seven-bottom mounted plough,

27-foot disc harrow, 40ft grain harrow, 20-foot tool carriers, 34ft field cultivator all large implements for their time.

The tractor was an instant success, which surprised some. An industrial version with off-set driving seat was introduced and was popular as an elevated grader and used mostly 23.5 x 24/5 rear tyres. An even heavier duty version was produced called the 700, but only 63 were made over the years. Many of the 5010 were exported principally to Western Canada, and a few were imported into the UK by various means, in fact more 5010s came to the UK than the 5020. There is some confusion with the 5010 serial numbers, which the industrial variations ran

All JD country music fans, Linda Burgess as the driver with Tony, Sarah (Linda's daughter) and Maurice Houghton all in the John Deere livery.

Technical specification

John Deere 5020	
Built	1966-72
Configuration:	Standard & Row crop
Engine:	531.6 cu in (8698cc) six-cylinder OHV four-stroke diesel
Transmission:	Eight-speed Synchro-Range
Electrical:	4, 6-volt batteries. From 1969: 2 12-volt batteries direct starting (serial no: T323R-025000)
Tyres:	F: 11.00 x 18.4-16 F: 9.50 x 20 R: 24.5 x 32 R: 18.4 x 38 (used normally for dual rears)
Weight:	17.920 pounds - 8136 kilograms

Hardly any of these tractors came to the UK new, but this example did, note the correct front weight.

A new speedo cable has been fitted and the tractor is correctly licensed under the Historic class, duty is not payable on pre 1973 machinery.

Another first since 1918 (All-Wheel-Drive tractor) was the no-clutching gear change, shift-on-the-go system also a power differential lock system was offered.

The original warning transfer has been kept and the code plate is underneath the top link.

Near side of the tractor showing the track rod and cast front axle cradle.

simultaneously. When production stopped some 5438 of the agricultural version had been made with around 1500 exported to places other than Canada. If you take the industrial versions around 7500 were made in total, not 9000 as I have seen quoted.

When the 20 series replaced the 10 series in 1966 the basic development for the 5020 was of course more power with an increase of ten percent and when tested in 1966 it produced 133.25 bhp and 113.72 dbh. The transmission was not altered and an auto transmission was not to be offered. However that was not to be the end of development for the 5020 as in 1969 a remarkable 121.86 draw bar horsepower was achieved and 141.34 belt horsepower, this was truly a 140 hp tractor.

In 1967 a so called row crop version was offered with a swept back front axle, to improve the manoeuvrability which in essence shortened the wheel base. Longer king pins and housings were fitted (3inch longer) and the front axle was adjustable from 64-81 inches. Also I see you could have a wider version from 71-88 inch and some, but not many, were fitted with rowcrop fenders and cockpit covers. However to find a version like this is very rare today. I would estimate one to be worth, with such fittings, in the USA, approximately £60,000 fully restored.

Without doubt more 5020s were made than the 5010 and production finished in 1972, the last example to leave the factory was T313R-311330R. Some would say the tractor had been underpowered as it had been built like a tank. Its replacement the 6030 was to be turbochanged and certainly sorted that problem out. A good number of 5010-20s were re-engined with would you believe V-4 and V-6 GM two-stroke engines

with Kinzie being the major converter of these tractors, but that's a story for another time. A small number of 5020s came to the UK including the example imported by John Deere 'guru' Don Macmillan (via Ireland) and made in December 1967 T323R-020319, which is now restored in Dorset.

The 1968 manufactured example (T323R-023635R) that we had come to see on Sunday 13 April, courtesy of Linda Burgess, Tony Macer and Maurice Houghton is another that worked in the United Kingdom from new. Kings Lynn, Norfolk is the place where this machine is said to have worked before ending up in a classic John Deere fleet at Church Farm near Wimple, Royston. Here it was used on a 1000 plus

acre farm along with a 5010, 4010 and 4020 to name but a few green machines.

According to John Deere expert Frank Summerlin the 5010, and the rarer 5020, did not go well in the clay soil of Bedfordshire, but it was at home in Norfolk. This example had been bought as a drawbar tractor and was used with double rollers for the latter half of its working life. It moved to the Burgess family ownership in June 2003, when Nigel Burgess drove it to its new home near Sutton. One or two repairs were carried out; including unseizing the linkage release cable and a new exhaust silencer was also fitted, besides an oil change. The alternator was replaced as were the two batteries, which sorted out the starting problem, ➡

Rear linkage has been put back to what it originally was, look at the quality of the paintwork with the Quik-Coupler 3-point hitch.

something you need right on such a monster as pushing a 5020 is not an option.

As time had gone on the 5020 had been put down the line, but a fuel leak developed to the extent that the tractor really needed sorting out before it could be used again. Keen John Deere fan and talented tractor/crawler driver Tony Macer with the help of master mechanic Maurice Houghton took the 'Giant of the Field' under their wings and in December 2006 when farming had quietened down, the intrepid pair took the panels off and drained the diesel fuel from the 48 gallon tank, which had split down the seam. Ben Burgess of Newmarket said they could do a proper repair so the tank was taken to them.

While this was going on it was decided the tractor really needed tiding up, so all the panels were taken off. It was found it really needed a set of rear tyres and eventually an excellent pair of 24.5 x 32 rear tyres was found for this machine by Ben Burgess, but don't ask how much they cost, even second hand, and as a precautionary measure new tubes were fitted locally. In the tidy up process the rocker cover gasket, the hydraulic steering main pipes were replaced and later the quick release spool valves were also, but the John Deere supplied ones would have cost £1200 so others were sourced. The brakes were good, however the air leak was sorted out as was the clutch pedal linkage, which Tony overhauled with new pins and bushes, and the wiring was tided up, although this is still an ongoing job at present.

Much rubbing down of the entire skid unit took place after harvest in July 2007, which took some doing as the tractor is huge and it was well covered in oil and dust, not forgetting the bird's nest. Tony who is 'head of operations' with the restoration of this tractor applied primer and top coat paint to the unit and it has certainly given the tractor something very special.

The link arms are huge, as can be seen in the picture, no problem lifting the implement up.

The 5020 needs some hard work to break the glaze from the cylinder liners to piston rings.

However from that moment in January 2008 it has been go, go, go in an effort to have the tractor ready for the Cottenham Road Run on Sunday 20 April 2008.

The panels had been taken to Kevin Knightley for sand blasting and priming at Chatteris, before they went to Andy Cole of AC Body Repairs at Manea, who has an excellent reputation for paint finishing, but specialises normally in Triumph TR6/7s. He straightened the bonnet and wings before applying 2-pack paint on the panels, they certainly took some litres. Andy did an excellent job for all to see, the paintwork looks light, it isn't heavy and just as it would have been when it left the factory.

The repaired fuel tank was fitted back in position and the fuel system was bled and cleaned up before any other work was undertaken, some thinners is ideal to remove any diesel stains when undertaking paint work as it will evaporate.

Some months later the job of collecting the panels was started. They were wrapped and wrapped in numerous blankets as any chip in the paintwork would have been disastrous. Do make sure the paint is hard before undertaking this sort of operation. By now the skid unit was all painted up in the correct shade of JD green something you have to be very careful with, as the later John Deere green is different to what was used in the 1960s and before. Maurice helped Tony fit the panels back on, this took some aligning, and a new exhaust manifold gasket was fitted at the same time. All went well and scratching of the vast panels was avoided, thank goodness.

The new drawbar was fitted on the back with the full category three and two linkage all in place and Maurice hand painted the wheels and hubs in the JD yellow, again the yellow is slightly darker on the older tractors compared to the present day range. Transfers were applied in the correct places, again you need to be careful to obtain the correct ones and do place then in the right positions as it will show in later times if they are not right. With the exhaust bolted back on it was time to introduce the 5020 back to the outside world and give it a road test, which happened in early April as Tony drove

the tractor out of the shed using the foot throttle (governor override). A foot throttle is something I like to have on all tractors.

A small party was put together to celebrate the completion of the project although the weather was not all that kind, the showers did ease by the end of proceedings. It was good to see those who have been very much at the hub of the project all together, principally Linda Burgess, Tony Macer and Maurice Houghton, they were joined by Richard, Carol, Sarah and Nigel for the great occasion and it was an honour to be asked to attend. We all had a wonderful afternoon enjoying the completion of the project. The 'Giant of the Field' is crying out for some heavy work as the cylinder bores are slightly glazed up and with any luck that might do the trick, mind you it will need plenty of implements behind it, but that will have to wait until later.

So what's next? Tony and Maurice are now turning their attention to the unstyled John Deere A, which is rare in the UK today. Nigel Burgess has made good progress, but owing to his work commitments and other projects he has not been able to spend time on it. We would all like to see it completed, particularly his mother Linda. Perhaps we will be able to have another party soon to enjoy more green and yellow, this time with only two-cylinders and steel wheels? Peter Love would like to take this opportunity to thank everyone mentioned for making this article possible. ■

Serial numbers

You can tell a standard from a rowcrop by the front prefix to the number shown: Standard: T323R, Row crop: T313R. The industrial models are enclosed in these numbers and not all the allocated numbers were actually taken up.

1966 – 12000-15559
1967 - 15560-20398
1968 – 20399-24038
1969 – 24039-26623
1970 – 26624-30002
1971 – 30003-30612
1972 – 30613-31130

Classic Series 4020 PFWD

In 1966 the 3020-4020 came in for a small revamp with more power from the engine now at 94hp, it carried a different block and more. However an option was offered with hydrostatic power front-wheel drive (PFWD) and at the same time as the changes the name Classic Series was added for the 1967-72 tractors. The four-wheel drive featured the adjustable front axle which provided adequate clearance for rowcrop work. A number of wheel and tyre options were also offered. This excellent example is part of the Deering collection in Northern Ireland.
Photo: Chris McCullough.

Mannheim's First Six Cylinder Unit

As the European JD Mannheim factory got its act together and gradually got over its problems, it was able to produce its first six-cylinder engine in the 4963 cc 86hp. Until it came along in 1969 and was said to be equal to the 4010. This superb example is owned by Herbert Epton of Carrington, Lincolnshire who has one of the best 'New Generation' collections of John Deeres in the UK today and sees Mick Herbert's assistant at the controls.   Photo Peter Love

DEERE'S A DREAM

A man who moved from owning a model to having the real thing talks to Joseph Lewis

Geoff Garrett says: "As a child my brothers and I were each given a special tractor model as a Christmas present. I had a die-cast John Deere 5020 and we played with the tractors in our sand pit at home. We probably moved around six tons of sand over the years.

"I promised myself that when I was older I would own the real thing. I could not find a 5020, so settled on a 6030, which was the next best thing; a natural progression as the 5020 became the 6030 in 1972."

Geoff's model was imported from Minnesota, USA. It was built in the first year of production and fitted with John Deere's A531 six-cylinder, turbo intercooled diesel, as used in the 7520 articulated model; this power was designed for heavy cultivation work in the big Deere's native prairies.

The tractor was in a poor state, mechanically and cosmetically, when Geoff got hold of it, with nettles growing up around the tyres. To bring his dream home to England the project started right away. Normally the model is on dual rear wheels, but 18 inches were removed from each rear stub shaft in order to fit the 6030 into the shipping container.

It was first brought into the workshop on New Year's Day 2006. The main problem was a bent crankshaft, which meant removing the engine and taking the tractor right back to the bare chassis to straighten it out. Geoff also had to line-bore the block and some parts, like the alternator pulley, proved impossible to find and had to be fabricated from scratch.

Evidence of heavy work was shown in the drawbar, which was so worn it was less than ¾in thick and had to be built up.

Now the restoration is complete, Geoff has a 6030 with two notable features. Firstly, the A531 engine is normally rated at around 175hp but Geoff's model was recently tested on a dynometer and produced 210hp at the pto shaft. This suggests that the flow on the pump was increased in the USA for even more pulling power.

Secondly, this 6030 came with a 3-point linkage, which is an unusual feature on a tractor designed with straight drawbar pulling in mind. Combined with the considerable horsepower this makes for interesting speculation as to the 6030's former use as it is normally a pulling tractor not a lifting tractor. ■

Geoff's 6030 is fitted with JD's A531 six-cylinder, turbocharged, intercooled diesel engine also used in the 7520 articulated tractor. Normally rated at 175hp this 6030 produced 210hp on a recent Dyno test; good for heavy cultivation or for testing a tractor pulling sledge. The American origins are clear in the sun canopy roof.

Hi-Clear
2520 Gas

The 2520 was introduced to farmers in 1968 following an upgrade of its predecessor. The 2510's four-cylinder petrol engine, that produced 54hp at the pto, was uprated to 61hp in the 2520. Diesel and LPG versions of the engine were also offered. This petrol example, built on 17 April 1969, is one of only seven Hi-Crop versions made with the Synchro-Range transmission and is part of the Keller collection.   **Photo: Peter Love**

Solid all-rounder

Peter D Simpson advises on a tractor that is now much sought-after

German John Deere 30 Series tractors were built in Mannheim, introduced in 1972 and manufactured until 1980, featuring eight basic models.

The three smallest tractors in the range, introduced in 1975, were the 48hp 1030, 53hp 1130 and the 59hp 1630 and these 30 Series tractors were ideal for the small-to-medium-sized farms of Europe.

The 1030 became a good all-round tractor, capable of many operations on the farm from pulling a three-furrow plough, through seeding and fertilising to mowing and grassland duties. With its three-cylinder 2,695cc John Deere-built engine, the 1030 has stood the test of time and is a relatively trouble-free tractor.

The original 30 Series was built in America and introduced in 1972. It retained the styling of the former 20 Series for the first three years of production but soon after its introduction the largest tractor in the line-up was released with a factory-installed operator cab to meet anticipated European sound requirements.

This module was called the OPU (operator's protection unit) and later on all models, down to the 1030, were factory-installed with it.

By 1977 the new-look 30 Series, including the 1030, had the option of MFW (mechanical front-wheel drive). The offset drive was a non-John Deere design but European farmers had been waiting a number of years for a 4WD tractor so it was not long before John Deere incorporated a powered front axle as an option on all its tractors.

When John Deere introduced it, the company described the 1030 as of solid construction, high quality and sound engineering to ensure a long, trouble-free life. How long was difficult to predict but John Deere dealers across the country at that time were promoted

The John Deere 1030 has a Hi-Lo transmission with four forward and one reverse speed in each range. Ideal for slow field operations such as rotovating and also high road speed work.

The John Deere 1030 has an extremely tight turning circle, ideal for turning at headlands or working in a rowcrop environment.

The OPU (operators protection unit) cabin is roomy with simple easily laid out controls.

as keeping parts in stock for at least 20 years after production ceased.

The ready availability of parts from UK John Deere dealers and the fact that parts from early production models and American-built tractors could be shipped in within a few days promoted faith in a reliable brand name which, coupled to a good back-up network, has kept many of these vehicles working today.

A tractor such as the five-year production run 1030 is still in demand from many quarters, despite it being 30 years old. The smallholder and small farmer find such a versatile tractor very useful indeed, capable of virtually any operation thrown at it. The tractor is cheap to run and maintain and, if kept in good order, will be worth far more to its owner than trading it in against a newer model.

Probably the newer, high-tech tractor won't have such a long life. The 1030 is a straightforward tractor with very few modern electrics and no computer controls.

As farms grow in size there is always a place for such a tractor. The 1030 will never be the main power horse on today's farm but such a 48hp machine makes an excellent yard tractor, which is also useful for topping roadsides and other light duties where the use of a more highly powered modern machine would be uneconomical.

The John Deere name has been trusted for so long that its green tractors with their yellow wheels have gained a strong following among both vintage and classic tractor enthusiast and owners.

Today classic tractors such as the JD 1030 are becoming highly sought-after by newcomers to classic tractors. In 1975 its price, new, was around £3,000. Price today for a good second-hand model is in the region of £3,500.

The 1030 is an ideal size for both road runs and working events, ensuring its current value will not drop.

The John Deere-built three-cylinder

engine, which operates at between 1,400 and 2,500 rpm, is rated at 48hp (DIN 46hp) and has proved reliable, offering quick, trouble-free servicing.

Looking at many of the engines on these older tractors, oil leaks are virtually none. When serviced to the manufacturer's recommendations the engine is virtually trouble-free. The three-cylinder engine offers a high 17.6 per cent torque reserve for maximum performance and pulling power with minimal gear changing.

Servicing and daily maintenance of the engine are quick and simple and the two side panels/screens of the engine unclip and can be totally removed, allowing quick and easy access to the air filter, radiator and fan belt.

Both oil and fuel filters are easily accessible and the engine oil drain plug is big and in a good position to get at. Overall the engine is good for the tractor operator to service and work on.

The eight forward and four reverse speed transmission gives a wide choice of working and road speeds. The field-proven constant mesh collar shift transmission with Hi-Lo with increased torque under load, enables the tractor to pull through tough spots.

A four-speed creeper box was available for slow operations, enabling the vegetable or specialist crop producer to work at very slow forward speeds.

The transmission on the 1030 is a mechanical shift with no electrics to go wrong and the centre-mounted gear levers below the steering column are short yet very positive to select and the constant mesh does make gear selection easy.

The closed-centre hydraulic system is very efficient - a constant pressure, instant action, power-on-demand system with a versatility that extends to every phase of tractor and implement control. The constant pressure variable displacement-type piston pump provides power where and when it is needed and has the capacity

to handle several jobs at the same time.

John Deere's lower link sensing of the three-point hitch can be adjusted to respond to soil density or changing ground contours automatically, either before work starts or on-the-go. The operator can select load control independently of depth control or a combination of both. On the 1030 the lift arms are strong with a lift capacity of 4,025 pounds (1,829 kg).

On an older tractor, check there is no play on the link arms and that the check chains are free and easy to turn. Always keep link arms, check chains and top link screw threads well greased to

The John Deere 1030 at 48hp is an ideal sized tractor for the small farm with a lift capacity of 4,025 lbs (1,825kg).

Specification

Horsepower

SAE (J816B)	48hp (35 KW)
DIN (70020))	46hp (34KW)

Engine

No. of cylinders	3
Bore and stroke	102 x 110 mm
Displacement	2695 cm³
Compression Ratio	16,2 : 1
Operating range	1400-2500 engine rpm
Torque reserve	17.6%

P.T.O

	Live or dependent 540 rpm rear or 540 rpm rear and 1000rpm front

Transmission

Type	Collar-shift, helical cut, constant mesh gears; optional High low
Final drive	Planetary drive
Brakes	Hydraulically wet disk brakes foot operated self adjusting, self equalising

3-point hitch

Load and depth Control	Lower link sensing
Category	I + II
Lift capacity (max)	17,9kN (1825 kp) (4025 lbs)

Hydraulic sysytem

Type	Closed centre

Shipping weight

(approx)	2140 kg (4715lbs)

Dimensions

Ground clearance under front axle	650mm (25,5in)
Overall length	3385 mm (133in)
Wheel base	2050 mm (81 in)

Load-and-Depth control for uniform tillage- automatically.

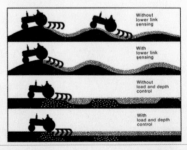

Load and depth control for uniform tillage. The JD lower link sensing system can be adjusted to respond to soil density or changing contours while on the go.

allow ease of adjustment. A single spool valve was generally standard with the option of fitting an extra spool valve. Operation of the rear hydraulics from the cab is simple and responsive.

When travelling on the highway the hydraulic wet disc brakes stop you safely and surely. The two pedal foot brakes make manoeuvring in tight spaces easy. When the pedals are locked together for road work a pressure-equalizing valve eliminates the possibility of one side braking harder than the other and causing dangerous swerving to one side. The self-adjusting, self-equalizing disc brakes run in a cooling oil bath and require no maintenance.

The standard 1030 has no power steering but this was offered as an optional extra, either factory or dealer-fitted.

Overall the John Deere 1030 is a

good, all-round tractor, which is simple to operate and easy to maintain.

Quality tin and paintwork have ensured this 30-year-old still looks good and doesn't show its age. If the small things like door hinges and rubber seals on the operator cab are maintained, the operator can work in comfort.

A well laid-out, simple rear end allows for easy implement attachment: keep all parts well lubricated and they will be trouble-free.

Keep the engine clean with all side screens in place and service the tractor to the manufacturer's recommendations and this tractor is capable of giving many more years of trouble-free service.

Thanks to Mark Bean Tractors (tel: 07957 856120), John Deere, Germany and Steve Mitchell, of ASM Public Relations.

I'VE ALWAYS WANTED ONE!

Peter Squires visits Andrew Bowring who had to wait a long time for his wish to come true when he finally acquired a JD 3130

Gotcha! After nearly 30 years Andrew has a John Deere 3130!

The name of Bowring has long been associated with agriculture in the Edwinstowe area of Sherwood Forest. Andrew Bowring of Ash Tree Farm has been working for his uncle Roy since leaving school in 1971 when he was 16.

"Roy always worked Ford tractors until 1980." Andrew told me. "As far back as 1976 I wanted a John Deere 3130, but they were fitted with 97hp, 6-cylinder engines and were considered too big for the farm.

As Andrew's 3130 was posed for a photo against the farm's recently-acquired 2005 John Deere 9780 CTS Hillmaster 11 it dwarfed the 3130 which looked anything but 'too big.'

"I purchased the 3130 (registered RFW 853R, serial number 210970) in April 2005 from JD dealers RBM of Clarborough,

Notts. It was first registered on 1st August 1976, when it was sold new by Alf Kitching & Sons of Crowle, North Lincolnshire. Until 2005, it worked in Goole and had just one farmer-owner from new."

LOW HOURS

The 3130 was traded in to RBM in a part exchange deal. It was Andrew's first sight of the tractor and fired up his ambitions of owning such a model.

"It had done just under 5,000 hours and had been very well looked after by its former owner," Andrew said. "One of the remarkable things I noticed was that it was all complete, nothing was missing or damaged."

After acquiring the tractor, the only work deemed necessary was a clean and a coat of paint, attention it soon received from Andrew.

On my visit, and eager to demonstrate his tractor, Andrew carried out a bit of cultivating with the JD3130 and a Twose Superflow 14-tine cultivator, to enable me to take some action shots. The original sliding rear window of the tractor's OPU cab let a bit of cool air in when needed. The 3130 has a 12-speed 'Hi-Low' ➡

On the farm, a New Holland 8080 unloads into a trailer hauled by a JD4240S.

Andrew's JD3130 stands beside the farm's JD9780 CTS Hillmaster 11 combine.

The German-built 7810 is seen at work on the farm with a Kverneland disc set.

Still in use today, one of Andrew's JD7810'S hauls a 4-furrow reversible Dowdeswell plough.

gearbox coupled to the 6-cylinder 5.9 litre engine. This offers a range of speeds with a suitable ratio for any operation.

Apart from a few changes (most noticeably the silencer) the tractor is very similar to the John Deere 3140 model; the 3140 2wd was the smallest option of the larger models but the farm's example was traded in for a 4wd version with SG2 cab. Two 4240S models followed, then a 4050, 7600 and a pair of 7810s, which are still earning their keep.

Today, these work regularly with a 6520, a 6420S and a pair of 3400 Telehandlers. Once Andrew was able to exercise his preference for John Deere motive power, all the farm's tractors have been supplied by RBM Agriculture.

THEN AND NOW
The 1976 JD3130 may once have been dubbed too big a tractor for the

farm but the family business recently added the JD9780 to its fleet of green machines. This monster has a 25ft, self-levelling header powered by the JD Power-Tech 6-cylinder turbo air-to-air aftercooled 8.1 litre (electronically-governed) engine powering a 3-speed, hydrostatic drive gearbox. A further 34hp is available for unloading the 10,000-litre grain tank during continuous harvesting. The operator can easily keep an eye on unloading through the cab windows, which give good visibility through just over 5 square metres of safety glass.

Andrew is married to Sheila, and their farm uses its John Deere fleet to work around 1,500 acres of arable land. The crops grown include potatoes, carrots and sugar beet as well as wheat, barley and oilseed rape . ■

The JD3130 with Twose Superflow cultivator.

The four wheel drive John Deere 4240S at rest between jobs on the farm

Andrew Bowring in the JD3130, cultivating the stubble in the autumn of 2005

Another job later in the year - the 3130 at work with the Twose cultivator

The tractor was supplied by Alf Kitching and Sons of Crowle, Lincs.

Michael's Green 8430

A The 8430 was thankfully saved by Michael Hoey, Rathmooney, County Dublin, Republic of Ireland as it was heading for a children's playground. The 1976 John Deere 8430 artic was only made from 1975-8 and featured the six-cylinder turbocharged 7.6 litre 156hp engine through the 16 speed Quad-Range gearbox. It's said the tractor worked in the UK mainland at one time, before crossing the water for the Republic of Ireland. Michael's team have tided the artic unit up and have used it on the land with the Simba discs behind which it pulled with ease.

Photo by Peter Love

Mannheim 4040 Buyers Guide

Andrew Hall says the Bruchsal, German made Sound-Gard cab is a plus when considering a hard to find Mannheim 4040.

The European 4040 was announced in 1977 and came along in 1978. It advertised with its contemporaries as 'New Iron Horses' with more horses and more iron!

The 4040 was marketed alongside the higher horsepower 4240 and 4440 and was a bit of a hybrid as it employed a USA-built transmission mated to a French-built engine from the Saran plant and assembled at the Mannheim factory.

The tractors were available in both two and four-wheel drive versions and used hydrostatic power to drive the front axles where equipped. Driver comforts were catered for by the Sound-Gard SG2 cab with the distinctive curved windscreen and one access door.

In common with most John Deere products, the 4040 was built to a high standard and embodied many features to keep it ahead of many of its competitors. The following information should assist anyone considering purchasing one of these classic machines.

ENGINES

The engine is a classic John Deere design of six-cylinder in-line with direct injection. Engines were turbocharged by a Garrett (Airesearch) turbocharger providing 110 horsepower at 2200rpm. Capacity of engines is 5.88 litres (360cu in) and fuel injection is provided for by a USA-built Roosa-Master injector pump feeding Bosch KDEL injectors.

If serviced regularly the engines will give many hours of work between major overhauls and have no particular weak points.

However when checking the engine externally do look for signs of head gasket failure or liner seal failure by viewing the condition of the oil on the dip stick, which is hopefully black in colour. However, if there are signs of white or grey then you more than likely have a problem of water in the oil, although John Deere engines are not prone to this if looked after well.

The engine should start readily with little cranking as it has direct injection, which normally gives instant starting. John Deere did supply a means of spraying engine starting fluid into the inlet manifold to assist cold starting but use of this should be avoided if possible, as with all diesel engines as they can get addicted and become very tired in a short space of time.

Coolant should be clean, preferably with anti-freeze to protect from frost and corrosion.

Fan belt tension should be adequate to drive the fan, water pump and alternator over tightening will cause undue strain particularly on the water pump and alternator bearings.

Access to the air filter is gained by pulling down the right hand grille panel and removing the dry paper-type filter element. The oil and fuel filters are readily accessed on the right-hand side of the engine and are easy to change. To give full protection to the engine good quality 15W40 oil should be used see oil level chart for quantity. Care should be taken to avoid overheating the engine oil when shutting down a hot engine by allowing it to idle for three to five minutes before switching off. This allows the oil around the turbocharger to cool and prevent over heating of the oil.

When starting from cold the oil should be allowed to circulate before imposing too much load. If these points are adhered to the engine should give little trouble. A worn engine may be difficult to start from cold and may emit blue smoke from the exhaust whilst running. If a 4040 engine requires a rebuild it is not beyond the capability of anyone with reasonable mechanical skills and does not require any special tools. However the 4040 is a large tractor so adequate lifting equipment is important with that six-cylinder engine.

CLUTCH

The clutch on the 4040 is a multi-plate wet-type, which was known by John Deere as the Perma-clutch. Its operation is hydraulic for both the transmission and the power take-off. The transmission is operated by the clutch pedal and the power take-off by a dashboard-mounted lever. The oil supply for the clutch is fed from the main hydraulic pump. Clutches on the 4040 model are extremely reliable and give little trouble in service, but do require some specific knowledge before any attempt to overhaul is considered.

TRANSMISSIONS QUAD-RANGE OR SYNCHRO

The Quad-Range transmission offered four ranges by means of two side-mounted levers providing 16-forward speeds, but reverse is only available on the lower three ranges, hence there are six reverse speeds. This transmission allows clutch-less changes between speeds one and two, three and four, but the clutch needs to be used between speeds two and three in the conventional manner.

In reference to the Synchro-Range that uses the standard eight-forward and two-reverse speeds working off one lever, it allows on the move changes. These are between first and third gear in station one, second and fifth in station two, fourth and seventh in station three and sixth and eighth on station four. However, shifts between stations, reverse or park require the tractor to be stationary have you got that! Transmission systems are robust and long-lasting providing oil and filter changes are carried out at required intervals. The 4040 benefits from having a de-rated engine compared to the 4240 and 4440 models and as such does not impose so much strain on the transmission.

POWER TAKE-OFF

Independent power take-off is provided through the hydraulically-operated Perma-clutch, engagement being by a lever mounted on the dashboard. Change of speeds between 540 and 1000rpm is accomplished by changing the output shaft on the tractor to suit the required speed. This is done by removing a circlip, withdrawing the shaft and replacing with the required shaft. Care has to be taken to ensure the replacement shaft is clean, as any foreign matter will contaminate the oil. Also, replacement needs to be done swiftly as there is a chance of losing oil and the pto hp is 90 at 2200rpm. Engagement and disengagement of the pto should only be applied at low engine speed. ➡

The left-hand view shows the compact Roosa-Master injection pump. The turbo-charger is situated above the exhaust manifold.

This right-hand view of the engine demonstrates the simple rugged design. Note the easy access to the fuel filter (top left) and oil filter (bottom right).

The hydraulic lift and spool levers are equally simple to use.

This rear view shows the pto-driven hydraulic pump and spool valve block for the loader to the left-hand side.

Gear layout on this Quad-range model is easy to interpret. Note the forward speeds in mph and km/h on the right-hand side.

HYDRAULICS & STEERING

Three-point linkage, offering category two and three, is standard on the 4040 with position control and depth control together with two spool valves for external hydraulic services.

The hydraulics are powered by an engine-driven pump and operate on the 'closed centre' system, which means oil is only pumped on demand as opposed to an open centre system where the oil circulates continuously and is returned to the reservoir. Power steering is employed on all 4040 models, in common with other John Deere tractors, and is powered by the main hydraulic pump where it has a priority flow. There are no specific problems associated with the steering and the system gives good service.

BRAKES

Brakes are hydraulically-operated wet disc and give long service life. Regular oil/filter changes in the transmission are desirable as metallic particles from worn brake discs need to be removed to prevent damage to other transmission components. Brake efficiency is good but wear will be increased if tractors are used to tow heavy unbraked grain or silage trailers.

WHEELS AND TYRES

Standard wheel equipment on the front is 10.00-16 with pressed steel front wheels and 16.9-38 cast rear centres with steel rims on sliding wheel hubs for track adjustment. Optional tyre sizes were 11.00-16 for the front and a choice of either 18.4-38 or 20.8-38 rear. Four-wheel drive versions use 12.4-24 front tyres.

CAB, CONTROLS AND TIN WORK

The SG2 cab is distinctive due to the curved windscreen and single entry door on the left-hand side. Access requires climbing the steps, and some people consider this a little awkward, but once inside it is an easy ride because the levels of comfort are high with a cloth-upholstered readily-adjusted seat and uncluttered floor. Main controls are positioned to the right-hand side and are clearly marked for the operator. On the Quad-Range transmission there is even a guide for the speeds available in each gear alongside the range lever. Air conditioning adds to operator comfort for those long hot days during harvest and vision is good, despite the presence of a pillar in the centre of the windscreen! Tractors with higher hours may require re-trimming of the cab, but the

Specifications

Engine horsepower	110@ 2200rpm
Pto horsepower	90@2200rpm
Transmission	16 forward/6 reverse Quad-range 8 forward/2 reverse Synchro-range
Hydraulic lift capacity	4300lbs (1950kg)
Pto Speeds	540/1000

Fill-up data

Fuel tank capacity	140 litres
Engine oil	13.5 litres
Cooling system	23 litres
Transmission oil	42 litres + 19 litres for Hydrostatic FWD

These machines have given Bill Wade good service and he finds them difficult to fault. In nearly 30 years of ownership he has not needed to replace a clutch or brakes on either of them.

relatively simple trim is easy to replace.

Tin work is similarly styled to other John Deere models of the period and is fairly durable with no specific areas of concern. Look out for impact damage to the rear wing tops as this is where corrosion can start and get a hold. Corrosion of the headlamps is not uncommon but replacements are available to keep a tractor looking tidy.

OWNER'S EXPERIENCES

The tractors pictured date from circa 1979; Bill Wade has owned them since they were about three years-old. They were originally supplied by Blythe & Pawsey, of Chelmsford, and cut their teeth on cultivations for potatoes in Essex. Bill used them in his arable business but these days they live a more sedate life in Kent involved in haymaking.

These machines have given Bill Wade good service and he finds them difficult to fault. In nearly 30 years of ownership he has not needed to replace a clutch or brakes on either of them.

One tip he does have, however, concerns the rear wheel rims. The steel rims are fitted to the cast centres with bolts and lugs. When tightening them he says each lug should be struck with a hammer after initial tightening and then tightened further to ensure they are tight enough as he has known the wheels on similar machines to work loose.

PRICES AND SPARES AVAILABILITY

The 4040 is not a commonly found model but examples do appear for sale occasionally. Prices vary from £5,000 to £6,000 depending on condition. Spares are available through any good John Deere dealer. Other parts specialists include Nick Young Tractor Parts, tel: 01673 828883, website: nytractorparts.co.uk and Cab Parts & Accessories, tel: 01873 811810.

In conclusion the tractors represent good value for money, are a classic already and well worth looking out for whether to work or play. ∎

JOHN DEERE PRAIRIE TRACTOR RESTORATION

Keith Harris of Silton Manor near Gillingham in Dorset needed a replacement for his ageing John Deere 8430. The move to an 8440 model became quite an operation, as Howard Sherren explains

Responding to demand, John Deere launched the 8440 and 8640 models in 1979 to replace the 30 series. The 8440 was a direct replacement for the 8430 and featured many improvements. Demand for these 'big' tractors increased dramatically as field sizes doubled and farm sizes jumped, but when the new 40 series was introduced in 1979, many farmers opted for the larger 275hp 8640 model. But the 8440 was still very popular and the further improved design made the range even more competitive, priced at around £25,000 before discount. It wasn't long before the 50 series replaced the

8440 and 8640 in 1982, when horsepower hit 370hp. Keith Harris bought his 8440 in January, 2005. Manor Farm is a 650 acre mixed farm, specialising in arable crops with around 200 ewe lambs. Varying soil types on some very steep hills give the tractors and machinery a real challenge. The 8440 is used predominantly on a 9 leg McConnell Shakaerator with a press or a 5m Vaderstad Rexius disc harrow. The Shakaerator had been extended 'in-house' to increase the working width and to harness the tractor's extra power.

A problematic 8430 model was the prime mover prior to the purchase of the newer 8440 model. Its dodgy engine and temperamental hydraulics made it a

continual headache and its replacement came sooner rather than later. Another big problem with the 8430 was that it was on duals, which made it difficult to move on the narrow lanes. Singles are unpopular in the US due to their tendency to bounce when working at speed but were an option in the UK. Some tractors were converted to singles but this one was originally supplied as such. Spotted on eBay back in December 2004, the 8440, registration LRC875W, failed to make its reserve price. After some investigation, Keith was able to track the tractor down to a recovery firm near Poole, Dorset, where it was bought for potential use as a recovery vehicle. Prior to this, the tractor was one of three articulated John

First seen back in December 2004, Keith Harris's 8440 was in a sorry state at a local recovery firm in Dorset.

Testing in spring, 2005, revealed a lack of traction to be a problem and further modifications were made.

Once home, the 8440's gearbox was opened up to find a badly damaged High-Low pack. This was repaired for just over £1,000 by using a second hand unit shipped from the US.

With the bodywork removed, operator Ivan began the mammoth task of preparing the tractor for re-painting. The chassis, wheels and rear fenders were given numerous coats of John Deere green and yellow on the farm.

Deeres which worked at Lambert Farms near Hull. Further investigation found that this particular tractor had been fitted with a new engine from a combine at around 5,700 hours and would be the best buy of the three.

The tractor looked a bit rough around the edges, but this was minor cosmetic damage which could be easily rectified. A noisy gearbox caused concern, but a deal was done and the tractor brought home. The problem appeared to be at the back of the gearbox. It is relatively easy to open up and take a look when the tractor is on full lock, as the rear of the transmission can be removed without splitting it. Unfortunately, the insides were a mess. The High-Low pack had disintegrated and bits were everywhere. At around £4,000 from John Deere, a new pack was an expensive answer and not cost effectiver. A second hand unit was eventually located at Worthington Ag Parts in the US and shipped across for around £1,000 and the tractor was

rebuilt. Testing in May with spring cultivations checked for any other problems. Although the engine was a later type, the horsepower was down, so it was decided to up the power levels to 250hp. This gave that little extra when the going got tough on the banks. The only other things of concern were the tyres, which were getting low on tread and traction was just becoming a problem. A set of part-worn 800/65 R32 Michelin tyres were found for around £600 each from J Brock & Sons. These really improved the looks, and more importantly, the traction, of the monstrous machine.

The newer engine was in very good order, so all that needed to be done was to fit a new exhaust and to rig up an electronic hour meter. The old engine had an analogue tachometer in the cab, so an electronic version from a combine was fitted in the dash. The tractor required a little more attention to the bodywork; paint had faded and was damaged in places. The tractor was stripped down to respray all the tin and chassis. The cab paint was good and was just polished up. Operator Ivan Brain took on the challenge of painting the chassis, fenders, grilles and wheels of the tractor, no small task. The tractor was steam cleaned a number oftimes before receiving a few coats ofJohn Deere green. Ivan produced an excellent finish on the paint work, although the bonnet and side panels were sprayed in two-pack by a local body shop to obtain a perfect finish. The front mesh ➡

The McConnell Shakaerator was widened in the workshop to harness the 8440's extra power and increase work rate of autumn cultivations.

A widened McConnell Shakaerator and press take care of minimal cultivations on Manor Farm in Silton, Dorset.

After the chassis and wheels had been painted, the fenders and bonnet were refitted. The bonnet and side panels were sent away to a local bodyshop for an expert, two-pack treatment.

Modified to around 250hp, the 8440 is a monster of a machine which you wouldn't normally expect to see in the South-West, and is certainly a sight working in the rolling hills of Dorset.

With the tractor complete and on a set of part-worn Michelin tyres, it was set to work with the 5m Vaderstad Carrier combination harrow preparing oilseed rape stubble.

panels are new. Six plough lights were found courtesy of a New Holland TF combine, while new indicator bars were made up for the front and rear. The cab interior was a mess, so a new cab cladding kit was found in the US, with other modifications, this transformed the working environment.

ENGINE

Fitted with John Deere's turbocharged and intercooled 466 engine, the 8440 produced 215hp at 2,100rpm as standard with maximum torque at around 1,400rpm. The bore and stroke are 116mm and 121mm. The 466 cubic inch displacement was comparable with most of the competition at the time. A 700 litre fuel tank kept the tractor going on long working days.

GEARBOX

A 16 forward and six reverse transmission was used in the 40 series. Known as the 'Quad Range', the gearbox was controlled by a single lever, which could select each range and speed. Four forward and two reverse speeds were available in each of the four ranges. The Hi-Lo clutch pack gave on-the-move shifts between speeds one and two or three and four. Unfortunately the clutch was required between speeds two and three, making it less versatile than a full powershift gearbox. Top speed was an acceptable 20mph.

A mechanical park brake was fitted and operated by the gear lever so operators would not engage it while putting the tractor in gear. Using John Deere's Perma-Clutch, smooth fluid action engages drive without jerks. The wet clutch design

is engaged and disengaged this way overheating is avoided and the clutch may last the lifetime of the tractor.

REAR LINKAGE AND HYDRAULICS

The Category III lift arms were capable of lifting 3,875kg, excellent for a predominantly drawbar-work tractor. A Quick-Coupler 3-point hitch made hitching large, heavy implements easy. Fitted with lower link sensing, the single system on the tractor provides realistic signals for the load or draft controls. Rate of drop and linkage sensitivity can be adjusted from inside and outside the tractor respectively. A 1,000 rpm PTO was available on both models if required. A closed-centre hydraulic system using a single

constant pressure pump was used instead of the alternative open-centre one. This gave the system more advantages for multiple-functions on high horsepower tractors. This system allowed hydraulic functions to be added or removed without affecting the others. By trapping oil between the pump and the function, the operation occurs instantly without delay and therefore oil does not over heat from constant pumping as in open-centre systems. Trapped at 2,250psi, the oil in the system ran at 2,000 PSI and was powered by a variable displacement radial piston pump. Hydrostatic power steering consisted of two large double acting rams which gave a 40 degree lock.

AXLES AND BRAKES

Weight was distributed at 60% to the front and 40% at the rear, so when under load the weight was transferred and distributed evenly. Rack-and-pinion 100mm axles were used for quick and simple track adjustment. By loosening three bolts and tightening two jackscrews, the wheel can be walked across the axle by turning the pinion. Dual wheels were standard; singles were available as an option but chosen by few buyers. Power brakes were fitted to the 40 series,

Although the tractor was almost 6m long, the machine was capable of turning in a radius of 5. 4m.

Originating from Lambert Farms in Hull, this 8440 was the best of the three John Deere articulated tractors used there. With a little time and money the tractor has been restored to an excellent standard.

Specifications

Model	8440
Engine Type	JD 466
Engine Power (hp)	215
Max Power @ (rpm)	2100
Max Torque @ (rpm)	1400
Number of ylinders	6
Displacement (cc)	406
Bore (mm)	116
Stroke (mm)	121
Fuel Tank Capacity (Litre)	700
Standard Transmission	Quad-Range 16 Forward x6 Reverse
Lift Capacity (kg)	3875
Turning Radius 4wd (mm)	5400
Length (mm)	5700
Width (mm)	2430
Standard Weight (kg)	9764
Std. Tyre Size Front	18.4 R34
Std. Tyre Size Back	18.4 R34
Cab	Sound-Gard

which gave excellent four wheel braking efficiency. The brake pedal operates three pistons which force brake shoes against a steel plate attached to the planet drive gear. Little effort is required, with maximum torque at 60lb applied force on the pedal.

CAB

The Sound-Gard cab was similar in style to the smaller tractors in John Deere's range. An awkward climb was required to enter the cab from the front and negotiate the dash to get seated. With sound levels as low as 80 dBA, the cab was a vast improvement over the previous 30 series. The HydraCushion Seat had a superior design to a standard seat. The suspension provided automatic weight adjustment with 'on-the-go' adjustable ride firmness which improved ride comfort. The tilt-telescopic steering wheel and orthopaedic support seat enabled operators to find the perfect driving position. The dashboard houses the PTO engagement lever and on the left, the warning lights are displayed along with four important analogue

gauges showing volts, fuel level, engine oil pressure and water temperature. The engine rpm gauge is installed to the right.

The John Deere 8440 is a flexible workhorse and at 215hp well suited to many farming operations. The improvements over the previous range makes it a lot more pleasurable to drive. Keith has been very pleased with his purchase and still considers it very good value, even after the amount of money spent on the restoration. The tractor will be seen at local shows in the future and is definitely an interesting and uncommon show piece due to its physical size.

ACKNOWLEDGEMENTS

Keith Harris for supplying photos of the restoration. ■

John Deere's HydraCushion seat gets thumbs up by operators. Automatic weight adjustment and on-the-move firmness control increases comfort levels.

Forward visibility was very good, but the curved front glass was not to some operator's liking. But the exhaust and precleaner were in line with the door frame reducing forward view obstruction.

The 16 forward and 6 reverse 'Quad-Range' transmission was operated by a single lever to the driver's right. Spool and linkage levers were also conveniently positioned on the side console.

Proud owner Keith Harris (centre) and operator Ivan Brain. Also pictured Keith's sons Tom, Robert, Charlie, daughter Ellie and Fergi the dog.

The rear view of the implement was excellent through the large rear window.

Simple and clear dashboard design has analogue gauges for all the vital information. Dashboard mounted PTO lever was typical of the SG cab.

John Deere '50' Series
3050 3350 3650 1986-93

The 50 series range from John Deere was introduced in 1986 to replace its 40 series. The 50s spanned a wide horsepower bracket, offering a tractor of a suitable size for nearly every operation.

The most popular of the three tractors in the six-cylinder range, the 100hp 3350 was one of the most reliable in its class of the late-1980s.

The 50 series could be considered as a 'love it' or 'hate it' affair by most users: many loved the engine and reliability that Deere gave, but others found the cab cramped and a bit too cosy. Looking back to the mid-1980s, the 50 series came as a replacement to the already well-established 40 series. The 50s were a vastly-improved machine based upon the 40 series, and using most of the existing design which had been tried and tested in previous years.

The range consisted of seven models from the 62hp 2250 up to the flagship 114hp 3650. The tractors sold extremely well across the country and the design needed very few changes. The main improvements which occurred over the production run happened in February 1991: the Prohytronic hitch control with electronic sensing became optional on the six-cylinder models which were ordered with High-Lift and 4WD. In September 1991 a few changes occurred to the renowned SG2 cab. 40kph transmission was now available on the 3650, front fenders became standard, a new digital tachometer,

larger wheels and air brakes could be fitted in the factory.

At this stage a new air cushion seal was also fitted which avoided the need for seat adjustments when operators changed tractors. With over 13,000 3650 tractors produced up until the end of 1993, the end was in sight for the range. The last 3650 went to a farming family in the Fishguard area in Pembrokeshire in February 1994. The 3050, 3350 and 3650 were all finally replaced with the 6000 series in late 1993. The models in this horsepower bracket consisted of the four-cylinder 90hp 6300 and 100hp 6400 in 1992, with the six-cylinder 110hp 6600 and 120hp 6800 appearing a year later. These new models became as popular as the range they replaced and soon became the market leaders for a number of years.

ENGINE
John Deere used a 5.9-litre, six-cylinder engine in these three models of the 50 series. The company boasted a low engine speed which in theory saved fuel, giving reduced vibration and improved engine life. Rated speed was 2,300 rpm, while the larger 3650 had a slightly higher 2,400rpm. One

litre per cylinder gave plenty of power with a reduced strain on the engine. 0.8 litres of fuel was saved due to the new 'Eco-Fan'. This was a viscous fan which automatically adjusted its speed to the actual cooling needs of the engine.

The engine featured wet sleeve liners, which – firstly – were easy to replace and secondly, dissipated engine heat into the surrounding coolant, thus improving engine life. Another interesting feature was piston spray cooling. Filtered oil was sprayed against the underside of each piston in the form of a jet. This cooled the cylinder and kept pistons and liners lubricated. The two smaller tractors were naturally aspirated; however, the 3650 was fitted with a turbo as standard. Fuel tank capacity was adequate for a good day's work at 173 litres on the 3650, although the 3050 and 3350 were deprived at just 121 litres without the optional tank fitted.

When looking over a machine today, check the gauges, as they are known to be temperamental. Engine reliability is extremely high as most engines are capable of completing hours of up to five figures or more before needing major work. Look out

The 3050 had a large physical size compare to its 92 horsepower. Despite this the tractor still sold well across the UK.

The range-topping 3650 achieved 114hp by adding a turbo to the 3350 engine. Fuel tank size was 170 litres, a lot more than the other two six-cylinder models.

Modified steps were introduced in 1992, the addition of a handrail and redesigned steps makes ascent and descent easier.

This M-registered 3650 has seen some work, yet it still holds its value. The last tractors to be produced are most desirable and demand a premium.

for engines which become hot and any with major oil leaks, as further investigation may be needed.

GEARBOX
The oil-cooled, multidisc clutch was hydraulically operated and could last potentially for up to 8,000 hours in the right conditions. Replacement could prove to be expensive and difficult. The previous tried and tested 'Power Synchron' transmission was continued from the 40 series. 16 forward and 8 reverse gears were available, from four gears with a splitter in two forward and one reverse ranges. The 'Hi-Low' ability to change up and down gears was handy feature, but not ground breaking, as it was already being offered by many of the other manufacturers at the time.

A modification to the 40 series gearbox was to integrate a shuttle reverser. This was formed by moving the reverse range to a position opposite the 'Low' range, which combined with 50 per cent faster speeds, produced quicker headland manoeuvring. A 30kph top speed was standard on early models, with 40kph an option, but becoming standard on the last few years of production

and offered for the first time on the 3650 in September 1991. The transmission is another very strong point and some describe it as 'indestructible'. Problems usually occur from wear in the selectors, which can be replaced. On the whole there is little to worry about in the transmission.

REAR LINKAGE & PTO
The John Deere three-point hitch, open-centre hydraulic system continuously sensed changes in the lower links, which produced immediate correction. This was unlike other open-centre systems which tended to produce a jerky movement, undesirable in tillage operations. Early 3050 and 3350 models had the option of the 'High-Lift' linkage, but this was standard on the 3650. The 'High-Lift' linkage enabled a little extra lift height, and the link arms also dropped all the way to the floor allowing easier implement hook-up. This feature became standard towards the end of production, with many of the tractors being recognised by the abbreviation 'HL'. Maximum lift was 4,900kg in the fully-raised position which worked out 800kg more than the standard linkage. The 3650 boasted a slightly higher 5,800kg lift capacity.

The SG2 cab… to most operators it's heaven, but some find it not to their tastes. Difficult access, lack of storage space and obstructed forward visibility are the main complaints.

Simple analogue gauges, 19 warning lights and PTO engagement lever sit to the left of the dashboard.

To the right of the dash lies the handbrake lever, tachometer, plough light and 4wd switches.

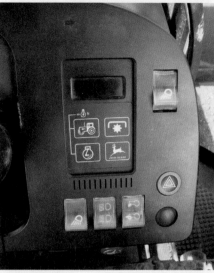
From 1992, John Deere fitted this digital dash which shows engine rpm, PTO speed, forward speed and tractor hours. A rare option fitted only to a few of the later tractors.

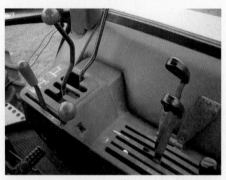
Transmission and hydraulic levers are all easily to hand on the right console and in use, give precise engagement.

HYDRAULICS
Prohytronic was introduced as an option on later tractors as an electronic sensing system. It gave accurate controls of the draft sensing, but was regarded as too complicated for the tractor and it is rare to find a tractor fitted with it.

The closed-centre hydraulic pump had a clever fuel-saving feature. The pump built up pressure until it reached the standby pressure and then rested. This meant that all the lines were held at the standby pressure without continuous pumping, therefore no overheating occurred. Once there was a demand, the pump instantly maintained a constant system pressure of 190 bar. The maximum pump output was 45L/min, good for the size of the tractor.

Pumps can wear out eventually and occasional trouble is not unheard of.

AXLES AND BRAKES
When first produced, the front axle provided one of the best turning circles on the market by using a 12 degree caster angle. Having the wheels on a slant while turning achieved a 50 degree steering angle and also allowed larger wheel equipment to be used, without reducing the lock. The turning circle was just 4.3m and 4.7m for the 3350 and 3650 respectively – excellent for a four-wheel-drive, 100hp-plus tractor.

The front axle was supplied by ZF, renowned for its reliability. The 3050 and 3350 were also available in 2wd form which gave even better manoeuvrability. Disc brakes were used in the rear, which were kept cool and protected by a continuous flow of cooled filtered oil. Retraction springs were also used to achieve definite separation of the discs after braking.

CAB
The existing SG2 cab which was used in previous years was fitted to the 50 series. Maximum noise levels were an amazing 80 db(A) – one of the best figures for the 1980s. A few improvements were incorporated into the older 40 series design, such as plough lights on each cab corner and extendable rear-view mirrors. Three awkward steps helped operators to enter the cab, which was improved and updated in 1992, and repositioned with an addition of a useful hand rail.

The SG2 was fitted with one door, which made up half of the curved front windscreen and removed the front 'A' corner posts. A unique design, only used by John Deere at the time, but it also created many enemies due to the poor access. This design meant that the door latching pillar was just off-centre of the bonnet, which along with the exhaust pipe and air cleaner stack

reduced forward visibility.

Once seated, the steering wheel had six position settings and an optional air seat from Grammar, which adjusted in seven ways and meant that operators were always comfortable. The left of the dashboard housed a large indicator switch, analogue temperature and fuel gauges with an array of 19 warning lights. The analogue tachometer, plough light and 4wd rocker switches were found to the right. Gauges have been known to cause problems and the fuse box was not as good as some.

The dashboard also housed the PTO engagement lever on the left and handbrake to the right, thus making them conveniently to hand. The gear, linkage and spool levers were found on the side console, all very accessible. Two wipers kept the front screens clear, while a three-speed fan and optional air-conditioning kept temperatures constant.

Look out for models fitted with the optional air-conditioning as this is now a 'must-have' for many operators.

DRIVING
Access to the cab is what could be described as 'hindered'. After negotiating the three steps, operators needed to shuffle through the door alongside the dash and manoeuvre through nearly 180 degrees to be seated.

How much?

Model	Year From	Year To	N	1	2	3
3050	1986	1992	£27,111	£8,500	£5,750	£4,750
3350	1986	1993	£28,728	£9,750	£6,750	£5,250
3650	1986	1993	£35,250	£10,500	£7,500	£5,750

(Guide – N: New price, 1: Excellent condition with no faults, 2: Tidy condition and usable, 3: Rough condition, for restoration or possibly breaking.)

Specifications

Model	3050	3350	3650
Engine Power (hp)	92	100	114
Max Power @ (rpm)	2300	2300	2400
Max Torque @ (rpm)	1400	1400	1500
Number of Cylinders	6	6	6 Turbo
Displacement (cc)	5883	5883	5883
Bore (mm)	106.5	106.5	106.5
Stroke (mm)	110	110	110
Fuel Tank Capacity (Litre)	121	121	173
Standard Transmission	Power Synchron 16F/8R	Power Synchron 16F/8R	Power Synchron 16F/8R
Lift Capacity (kg)	4900	4900	5800
Turning Radius 4wd (mm)	4300	4300	4700
Length (mm)	4787	4787	4787
Width (mm)	2037	2037	2267
Standard Weight (kg)	4475	4860	5125
Std. Tyre Size Front	12.4 R28	13.6 R28	14.9 R28
Std. Tyre Size Back	16.9 R38	18.4 R38	18.4 R38
Cab	SG2	SG2	SG2

This was not very convenient if the operator was in and out of the cab on a regular basis.

The standard seat was very comfortable and with the steering column, it takes seconds to adjust to a perfect position. Views visible around the tractor were excellent, as middle 'B' and rear 'C' pillars were narrow and side windows, large. However, front views were quite obstructed by the door pillar, exhaust and air cleaner. This small problem could probably be forgiven for the excellence of the rest of the cab.

Once started, the clutch felt smooth and accurate, while the range and gear levers moved precisely into position within their gate. When moving, the Power Synchron splitter worked efficiently and the brakes felt precise. Steering was very impressive and was so good that it definitely could be compared to a 2wd tractor, as headland turns were completed with ease. The engine pulled extremely well and felt like it had plenty of power in reserve. Linkage and spool levers were again simple and very easy to use.

Criticisms included: an irritating hand-operated diff-lock lever fitted to tractors from 1991, which was different to the earlier tractors. Cab space was limited, therefore an extra toolbox or hand luggage would need to be relocated outside the tractor.

VERDICT

The 50 series had the highest reliability levels in its class, which is ideal if you require dependability and simplicity. From the tried-and-tested mechanics of the 40 series, this tractor range shows no real weaknesses in its overall design. The only problems that might be encountered would relate to operator preference. The difficult entry, diminished forward visibility, and lack of storage space may put some buyers off. If the operators are willing to sacrifice and ignore these problems, then the 50 series could be the perfect classic machine. Resale values are still quite high and are likely to maintain these levels or perhaps increase – considering the strength of the classic tractor market. Rough early examples can be found for around £4-5,000, with tidier, usable tractors fetching £7-8,000. The youngest 1993 models (33 and 3650) are most sought after by collectors and enthusiasts, and demand the higher premium. L registrations and some M-plated tractors can fetch up to a staggering £12-13,000 if in mint condition.

As time goes on, the popularity of these tractors will definitely increase, as it seems they are likely to last forever. ∎

ACKNOWLEDGEMENTS

Thanks to Steve Mitchell for supplying technical information.

Contacts

Addisons – Dismantling 50 Series
Tel: 01652 618661

Alexander & Duncan Ltd
Leominster, Herefords Tel: 01568 613 434
www.alexanderandduncan.com

Ben Burgess
East Anglia Tel: 01603 628251
www.benburgess.co.uk

Brede Valley Tractors JD Specialists
Tel: 01424 882442

Cornthwaites
Preston, Lancs Tel: 01995 606969
www.cornthwaites.co.uk

Burden Brothers Agri
Isle of Sheppey, Kent Tel: 0195 880224
www.burdenbros.co.uk

J W Doubledays
Holbeach St. Johns, Lincs
Tel: 01406 540293 www.jwdoubleday.co.uk

Farol Ltd
Oxfordshire Tel: 01844 278843
www.farol.co.uk

Masons
Newton Abbot, Devon
Tel: 01626 852140 www.jamesmasonltd.co.uk

Meath Farm Machinery Ltd
Navan, Co. Meath Tel: 042 9666386/357
046 9023946/28244

Rea Valley Tractors
Pontesbury, Shrops Tel: 01743 790801
www.rea-valley-tractors.co.uk

Nick Young Tractor Parts –
Holton Le Moor, Lincs
Tel: 01673 828883

Comments

Likes	Dislikes
✔ Reliability	✗ Cramped SG2 cab
✔ Simplicity	✗ Forward visibility
✔ High-Lift hydraulics	✗ Bonnet mounted fuel filler

Parts

	3350
Engine Oil Filter	£4.99
Pre Fuel Filter	£3.20
Secondary Fuel Filter	£10.99
Transmission Filter	£8.75
Hydraulic Filter	£36.75
Inner Air Filter	£21.50
Outer Air Filter	£24.50
Fan Belt	£12.50
Clutch Disc	£225.00
Starter Motor	£210.00
Alternator	£160.00
Water Pump	£510.00
Hydraulic Pump	£1240.00
Exhaust Pipe	£97.00
Exhaust Silencer	£235.00
Mirror Glass	£16.99

(Retail prices direct from John Deere, excluding VAT, depending on specification)

The highest tractor in the John Deere 'New Generation' display was Henry Dixon's 1962 4010 diesel hi-clear.

Go Green! The largest display in the United Kingdom so far of classic John Deere tractors was staged at the Somerset Vintage Tractor Show on 6-7th February 2010, thanks to the efforts of section leader Tony Adams, writes Peter Love.

To assemble what Tony did was something very special indeed and thanks to Nigel and James Hutchings to name but two, the 50th anniversary of 'The New Generation' of multi-cylindered John Deeres was celebrated as never before.

Some 53 John Deeres were assembled inside and out of one of the exhibition halls at the Bath & West Showground, Shepton Mallet, Somerset. Now with all the JD ephemera inside it transformed the building into a 'Green Heaven' which the many West Country JD fans enjoyed to the full.

A number of two-cylinder examples were assembled and on show as well, but the classic era tractors were the stars here, particularly the 30 and 40 series, many having been recently retired or in some cases are still working. The whole display was an education in itself with the 'New Generation,'

'Generation II', leading on to a 6600, part of the 90's revolution, before more modern products outside like the current 8345R.

In some ways the colours used today by the company are similar to when tractor production took off with the purchase of the Waterloo Gasoline Engine Co, Waterloo, Iowa in 1918 and they still certainly stand out from the crowd. In this, the 21st century, these two elements are nothing but eco friendly to the environment we live in, which just shows how that famous individuality has kept the company ahead in so many ways. That very much stems from the 'New Generation' which was put on line in 1960, some 50 years ago and as other companies floundered John Deere has not looked back.

In respect to John Deeres being sold in the UK, the Waterloo Gasoline Engine Co's was sold in the UK and Ireland as the Overtime and assembled at L J Martin's works at Hounslow, London. It is said that over 3,500 came to these shores during World War One

in the single-speed R configuration and the two-speed N. Even after the John Deere takeover of this company on 14th March 1918 for $2,350,000 the tractors still came to the UK including those with the late automotive steering and riveted frame.

However after that, and with the economy the way it was, John Deere tractors did not reach these shores very frequently. In 1935 the first importers came along, particularly Jack Olding and then people like FA Standen sold John Deere's in some numbers from the standard AR, AO, BR, BO and the rowcrop AN and BN. A few three-speed D's also arrived and of course the small L. However under Lend Lease that all changed and the numbers dramatically increased under the styled range, even the mighty G, the last to be styled in 1941, came here. Mostly though a good helping of D's and various rowcrops came in some numbers at that and went mostly to East Anglia.

Over the years I have presented a number ➡

George Woolgrove from Oxen brought along his mighty impressive 4630 made from 1972-77 and all in working clothes.

The John Deere story was brought right up-to-date with the 8345R.

Oldest tractor in the John Deere display was the Smith family's 1919 Overtime N.

Representing the just post war period for John Deere was this fine M that was made 1947-52.

For a number of people the BR and AR were the first types of John Deere's they came in contact with during the 30's, imported by Jack Olding.

What a stunner! The rare to see even in the USA, 2510 four-cylinder gas of Henry Dixon.

John Deere bikes are popular, this example being one from the Henry Dixon collection.

of pioneer British JD 'guru' Don Macmillan's, slide shows and Don told everyone how he started out as a young ploughing contractor in 1942 for the War Ag. He used a Oliver 90 and came from Gloucestershire to work in Wiltshire where he was given plenty of work using a Ransomes Multi-trac four-furrow plough. The Oliver could cope, but was very uneconomic and in 1943 Don was allocated a styled D 154757. He had already made contact with John Deere who invited him to visit the works after WW2, which he was to do in the autumn of 1947. However, before that happened, he ended World war two with three other JD's in the fleet - two being second hand, the unstyled BW and D. He was able to purchase new a steel wheeled A, that was to gain pneumatics and extra gears. By

then Don had two combines in action but not from JD yet.

Besides contracting he went farming with the purchase of a 220 acre farm where his 15 staff could spend their winter time working, before contracting again during the spring, summer and autumn months. Sadly owing to post war import restrictions and monetary considerations the make as such was not sold in the UK directly. In fact John Deere did set things in motion to build tractors from the UK, from a manufacturing plant near Glasgow, Scotland. Unfortunately things didn't progress well with the bureaucrats of the time. Deere & Company went elsewhere and purchased the Heinrich Lanz factory in Mannheim, West Germany, which in 1956 was very run down. It remains today the

most modern tractor factory in Europe and is Deere's main European manufacturing base.

During the 50's Don took over the original UK importers two-cylinder stock and everyone came to him for spares, he became a large second hand combine dealer selling many JD 12A trailed combines along the way. He became Britains first post war JD official dealer, but didn't have any new tractor stock until basically 1962 and then the story really started.

However it would be in January 1966 that John Deere Limited commenced trading from its present day headquarters, a former World War Two bomber base, at Langar, near Nottingham, and as they say the rest is history.

In many ways John Deere had a head start in the West County of Great Britain thanks

The 1120 came out in 1967 and was called the 1520 in North America.

Gordon Cox and his 1952 R diesel still in its original clothes.

The Classic Series 4020 4 x 4 came on stream 1967-72 and this example is coming back together in Stephen Batten's hands.

Top implement at the show went to Nigel Hitchings JD baler.

Bought as a 25th wedding anniversary present Malcolm 'H' tells me, fitted with a winch and a genuine Somerset WW2 import of 1944.

Jason Smith (right) with Gordon Griffin and Jason's styled G finished hours before the show and a western Canada import from Stan Kick.

'Best in Show' went to Ian Treviss 1976 JD 4230 two-wheel drive KHW 832P.

to the efforts of Don Macmillan. At the show three John Deere main dealers provided modern machinery and stands, Ashworth's of Chedder, Smarts of Dorchester and Hunts of Tilshead and were all made very welcome.

Just walking in the building and looking at the 'New Generation' was a stunning and exciting feeling to any John Deere fan and user. There were many awards to be had here at the show and John Deeres did very well indeed.

The winner of the 'Off Farm Class' was Alan Sprack's lovely 1982 John Deere 1640 now in its fourth ownership. The model came out in 1982 and was around until 86. Fitted with the four-cylinder 62hp engine, which has plenty of 'grunt' with the 16-speed transmission and this example has around 6460 hours on the

clock. It's fitted with a 175 loader on the front and at one time the tractor was out of use for eight years. It was bought by the current owner in 2006 and besides batteries, fillers etc it has been a cheap tractor. However the front half of the roof has been replaced and the cab lining now needs sorting. It's used by Alan on a circular log splitter and was supplied originally by Ticknell's.

James Hutchings, like his father Nigel, is steeped in John Deere tradition and James 1992 3650 K884GYD was to take first place in the 'Best Working Tractor' class. The 3650 came along in 1985, was around for eight years and its six-cylinder turbocharged engine was a powerful tractor with 114hp, but could be rather 'juicy'. One has to say the Power Synchron 16/8 transmission was

a good piece of kit. Third in the class was 'Tonka' (Tony Adams) own tractor, a 1993 '50 Series Task Masters' 3350 L804RBP, which he has owned for just over a year now and has enjoyed it to the full. Nigel Hitchings was to take first place in the implement class with his JD K56 baler that was positioned behind his 1968 2020 LFX733G, a lovely piece of original kit, including the Duncan cab. It was made the first year of Mannheim production for this model and was to be around until 1971.

'Best Restored' saw Ian Treviss 1976 4230 KHW832P two-wheel drive finish third, what a lovely restoration has been done on this tractor by the father and son combination. Certainly an advanced 'looker' for 1972 when the 'Generation II' range was shown to the public in Saarbrucken, Germany for the first ➡

Tony Adams known to so many as 'Tonka' did a superb job in Somerset and is seen moving an immaculate 2030.

Lining up in the show arena took some doing, but the final outcome was good with the 3140 made at Mannheim 1979-86.

'New Generation' the sign of new beginnings for John Deere.

Another tractor to arrive in preservation last year is this superb 2020 RPO638K of George Woolgrove.

The Marsh's took first place in the model section of the show.

time. It was later to take the converted award of 'Best in Show', a very pleasing result for the many JD classic fans here.

Third in the 'Concours' was George Woolgrove's just restored and beautiful 4230, which he still uses for corn carting and rolling and came from Robert Fearnley in 2008. George is a keen John Deere fan and has some lovely kit which he showed here. I for one certainly appreciated him including his 1968 2020 with 6390 hours on the clock, which worked on the Cotswolds and is now in preservation. His 1976 4630 again was

great to see and came from the 'Joan of Arc' country of Reims northern France with 10167 hours on the clock. Since 2006 it had worked in Cheshire before joining George's stable in December 2009.

Another new tractor on show was the Tom Price 1989 4755 G127OKH monster from south Wales. The 4755 had been bought from Scotland in December as well and again is in excellent order, so surprising as the rust has dire affects north of the border.

Talking of Wales and Pembrokeshire, top cattle farmer Henry Dixon was here with

his 1962 diesel 4010 hi-clear. It was the most spectacular model at the show, as it does feature a 'lady' driver on the footplate. However an over looked tractor in the JD history is the 2510. Henry's lovely Powershift example is totally original with the four-cylinder gas 54hp engine, eight-speed transmission. This for many was a first time view and a lovely import from North America, a model only made from 1965-68. What a stunner and totally original, quite frankly it must have been misunderstood by the judges as this tractor is of the highest order.

What a line up! Something that will be hard to repeat for some time that's for sure.

Generation II styling on the 1977 930 that more than likely had a cab when new.

Geoff Garrett's 6030 is a handsome beast, all 'brute force.'

Malcolm Jay's 2650 G927XDX is a type that came in 1987 and featured the 78hp engine.

Smallest tractor in the John Deere display was the 185 hydro.

The late 60's saw the turbocharged 2120 come along, made until 1972.

The 720 shows the 1957 style and original condition with power steering.

Looking a 'proper' machinery is the 90's revolution 6600

Tom Price 1989 4755 G127OKH monster from south Wales. The 4755 had been bought from Scotland in December

Biggest classic monster at the show is the 8440 artic which came on the scene in 1979.

The Stuckey's Wheatland 4020 is a gem of a tractor and typical of what you can find in North America.

A name from the past now Ticknell's were big when it came to John Deere's for a number of generations.

Percy Grant had his lovely 1952 R here, which the engine and donkey having needed much work along with the original example of Gordon Cox next door. The man who has done so much for classic John Deere collecting Ivor Grant brought along a number of his machines including his 5020, a genuine UK import and said to be the first to arrive in the UK. Also his lovely 4240, 2030 and 1020 which was to win 'Post Vintage' and he has more at home! Stephen Batten had his winning M, and 4020 Classic four-wheel drive (PFWD) here that came from a Cheffins sale last year, another that looked a treat. Geoff Garrett was also about with the mighty 6030, which he has been through a lot with to get it

to where it is now particularly the engine.

The ultimate just had to be Keith Harris from Dorset mighty 8440 artic that is for sale, tel: 07966166905. They were known originally as the 'New Iron Horses' range and were the giants in the fields made from 79-82 at the Waterloo factory. This example looks wonderful and is ideal for large acreage in the West Country that's for sure.

From large to small as two excellent John Deere model collections were seen and both were superb, but the husband and wife duo of the Marsh's took first and electrician Simon MacDonald was to be third.

There were many more that have been left out, but Nick and Henry Young had a

wonderful show with their classic JD spares stand. The smallest in the classic tractor range had to be the 1977 930, which came in during 1975 and a Mannheim product. However the actual smallest JD four-wheeler on display was a Hydro 185 grass care machine that looked very smart and was actually for sale, tel: 07831347400.

It was a wonderful show and the John Deere participation set it all apart, as significant history was made by this display. This was the very first 'proper' classic JD show of its type to take place here in the UK and Republic of Ireland. It has set new standards for others to follow 'The New Generation' has certainly arrived. ∎

Deere to his heart

Joseph Lewis speaks to Ivor Grant about his John Deere 4240, first seen in January 2007 on a road run in Somerset

Ivor Grant was a slaughterman, who helped on the company's farm near Taunton when the meat trade was quiet, and eventually became its manager.

He said: "Some 30 years ago we began with a JD 2130, which was a big tractor then and used for ploughing and everything else, a real all-rounder.

"We then had a 3130 because we were doing 700 acres of our own forage harvesting, so we needed a big tractor.

"We had always used John Deeres and replaced the 3130 with a 4240 - possibly the biggest model we could source locally, especially as most local tractors were on dairy farms. Ours was an S registration, around 1978, and I believe an all-American version. The 133hp, six-cylinder non-turbo engine was very smooth as I drove back on the road from the depot, especially with the QuadRange transmission. We would start at 7am, top up the diesel in the day and work until 10 or 11 at night.

"We also had a John Deere 2140 and a couple of Internationals. On the whole estate across Somerset we had 21 tractors."

Ivor's tractor collecting started around 27 years ago when he was offered a 1949 Field-Marshall Series II contractors model for £475, which it was a job to afford in those days. A Fowler VF came along at the same time and other crawlers included a David Brown 30 TD, which was restored and then sold on.

Ivor has also restored two John Deeres for the green and yellow oracle himself, Don Macmillan - a model L unstyled and a model A.

His current collection includes two other John Deeres. First came a 2120 from 1972, originally supplied by Don Macmillan and used as a yard scraper near Wellington Monument. Ivor paid £600 and restored it in six months to Canadian specification with fan wings.

John Deere 4240 first registered on June 1, 1982. YBM 242X, number 343448L, is pictured in February 2007 after considerable tin work and cab restoration. This view also shows the 4240 is a fairly long tractor.

Bonnet removed and ready for the steam cleaner. The six-cylinder 133hp non-turbo engine was mechanically sound. Straw had to be removed from all the filters. Note cab door (and mice nests) removed for restoration.

First time out at Taunton New Year's Day Road Run - a proud moment. Also a first for driver David Chapman. Is this the SG1 cab as it appears to be slighter taller than on later 2140s? Can any readers help?

This is why we do not paint in February (moisture). A heavy rub down has given a good finish. Ivor is looking for front weights.

Close-up of the six-cylinder, 133hp non-turbo engine. The engine would not run cleanly as the diesel filter was clogged.

Dashboard controls are simple and straightforward with dashboard-mounted PTO lever.

Sixteen speed QuadRange transmission makes the 4240 a very smooth tractor to drive. All controls fall easily to hand.

A pretty compact linkage and drawbar for such a big tractor. There are still a couple of the 4240's four spool valves to sort out and some minor oil leaks to rectify.

The other is a 5020 from 1966, which is significant because Don Macmillan's records indicate that SNT323R013416R is the first 5020 originally imported into the United Kingdom.

Ivor took his John Deere 5020 to Tractor World at Malvern, where he met a contact who knew of his interest in 4240s. Two weeks later he was invited to "come and have a look".

At first glance, Ivor was a little doubtful – "It was a little rougher than I had thought."

It had two major problems. The first was the cab. At some stage the exhaust was bent back and left blowing on the roof, which had melted the inside and outside of the cab. At £300 for a new roof, Ivor nearly didn't buy it.

The second factor was the wings which, completely rusted out, would have to be replaced. The front lights were also smashed and would need to be replaced.

However, a closer look revealed a mechanically sound 7,000-hour tractor, on the original engine, with a few minor oil leaks on good 50 per cent tyres, front and rear. The QuadRange transmission was also fully functional.

Significantly, the only difference from Ivor's "original" 4240 appears to be the door lever. The 1978 model was a pull-down lever, 343448L, first registered on June 1, 1982, is a push button.

The tractor (YBM 242X) arrived at Ivor's home in Somerset in January 2006 and, working two hours a night and taking part in rallies in between, it took him 11 months to restore it.

With the bonnet off, the first task was a thorough steam clean. All the filters were choked with straw, suggesting the tractor had worked on either a straw chopper or baler. Badly stone chipped, the bonnet had a good rubdown prior to painting. With only a couple of oil leaks, mechanical work was minimal.

Initially, parts for the 4240 proved difficult to find but, without an internet connection at home, Ivor used local contacts, telephone or fabricated his own pieces where required.

The majority of the time was spent on the cab. The roof was repaired by rolling a piece of metal over it and melting it into place,

Ivor's John Deere 5020 serial number on the largest of the 20 series.

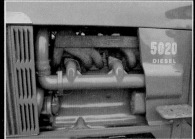

A standard 5020 six-cylinder engine is rated at around 130hp. Before Ivor bought his significant find, a turbo was fitted, boosting power to 180hp.

The supplier's plate shows Ivor's 5020 which came from Drake & Fletcher of Maidstone, Kent who were also Bedford agents.

He will not change these in a hurry! The 5020 rear tyres are ballasted with the proper solution. Each rear has a 1,600lbs inner wheel weight and three outer wheel weights. The two rear wheels, combined, weigh around four tons.

Ivor Grant with what is believed to be the first John Deere 5020 originally imported into the United Kingdom in 1966, registration HKT 85D. It was used on autumn cultivation with a Simba heavy duty cultivator. Note the John Deere roll bar from the USA.

then painting it. This section was originally plastic with a John Deere top coat. A new exhaust was also required to replace the previous owner's temporary effort.

Prior to restoring the cab interior, a number of mice nests were removed from the top of the radio and under the roof line. This suggests barn storage for some period of time.

Completely new cab cladding came from Uphill Sales and Service, of Urchfont, near Devizes, Wiltshire - the original cladding was ripped to pieces and would not have done justice to the restored exterior.

Inner and outer wings were particularly difficult. Ivor fabricated and welded the inner wings and new outer wings came from Nick Young and further afield from John Deere in the United States.

New door surrounds were fitted around the original glass and the original seat received a new cover to complete the cab's makeover.

All four "height-lights" on top of the cab had to be replaced, which may suggest a hard working life.

Ivor's first 4240 was supplied by Tincknells, of Galhampton. "We do not know who supplied our restored 4240, but we obtained possibly some of the last Tincknells badges from their sale in November 2006 to complete our memories," said Ivor. This was a fitting finishing touch.

The "came-with" 11x16 front tyres and 18.9x38 rear tyres were found to be in good order and did not need changing.

With the cab almost complete, Ivor wonders if this was an SG1. The cab is slighter taller than on later 2140s. Ivor emphasises attention to detail - "we had a number of little jobs, which if left, could have spoiled all the hard graft. The wiper shaft out of the motor had broken off. We drilled and welded a new piece. I was also putting a wire up for the flashing light and took a rust pimple. This started to leak, but we were able to fabricate a new part."

The John Deere 4240 is a great road run tractor and straightforward to drive. This was shown in the Taunton Road Run when David Chapman used the 16-speed QuadRange transmission for the first time.

In simple terms, there are normal 1,2,3,4 gears, with an A,B,C,D in each gear. The clutch is required when changing from 2-3, but not for 1-2 or 3-4. Reverse is only in A and B, but the operator can still "tap" across in reverse for higher ratio. In the same way, coming up a steep hill, you do not need the clutch, but can simply tap the lever across to eliminate the need for losing momentum by declutching as would be the case in a car.

John Deere's other 4240 transmission was Powershift, where the operator kept pushing forward - in a similar manner to a motorcycle's sequential gearbox. ∎

John Deere 55 series
4755/4955 1988-1994

There aren't many tractor ranges considered as 'old American muscle', but the 55 series from John Deere certainly fits the bill. With a design dating back to 1983, these thoroughbreds were well suited to the open plains of the US, and proved very popular at home in Britain in the early 1990s. Although there aren't many now which head the tractor fleet on arable farms, they do certainly have a 'classic' appeal and look to be a safe purchase if you are looking for plenty of poke. Howard Sherren investigates

The 190hp 4755 and 228hp 4955 were built from 1987 to 1994 and were one of the last ranges to feature the legendary SG2 cab

John Deere began its legendary design back in the 'seventies with the 30 and 40 series tractors. This gave them a base platform with which to improve design and build bigger machines. The demand for higher horsepower, more efficiency and better performance had increased greatly through the years, so improvements would have to be made by Deere to keep its share of the market. The original 40 series was made in Waterloo, USA back in the early 1980s.

After a few years, John Deere decided to introduce a new range of higher-powered tractors which incorporated the older design with many improvements and new features. So the 1983 50 series models were born and built in Mannheim and Getafe, Germany.

The models produced were, the 4050 which gave 128hp, the 4250 gave 144hp, and 161hp was achievable from the 4450. The biggest machines, the 4650 and 4850 had an output of 190hp and 215hp respectively. Only available in 4wd, the tractor's power was found to be favourable for heavy arable work and big square baling. Few machines were imported, as many users found them too big and difficult to manoeuvre in Britain's small fields and narrow roads. In 1987 the 55 series was introduced in the United States, although it was not brought to Great Britain until late-1988. The 55 series offered more power, and again improved operation. The model range consisted of the 4055, 4255, 4455, 4755 and 4955. The engine's powers are 128, 144, 160, 190 and 228hp respectively. This range was manufactured until 1992, when the 4055, 4255 and 4455 were dropped in preference to the new 6000 and 7000 series tractors. The 4755 and 4955 continued on through to 1994 when they were replaced with the completely new 8000 series. The introduction of the 55 series gave a few new features to the tractor range. The largest model in the range, the 4955, had 13hp more than the 4850, with the other models unfortunately gaining no increase. In the cab, the dashboard had the new "IntelliTrak" system which was an improved version of the "Investigator 2" system. It offered the same features as the previous version, but was all digital, giving clearer and more precise readings. There were relatively few problems with these tractors, but most were sorted out in the last series of machines. The problems solved were: oil and air filter repositioned, exhaust stack repositioned, better steps and access to cab. One feature which wasn't corrected was the fuel tank location. This was located right at the front, on top of the bonnet which made filling extremely difficult.

Also, the SG2 cab often proved difficult to get in and out of when entering and exiting lots of times, manoeuvring around the dashboard could get tiresome.

ENGINE

The 4755 and 4955 came fitted with a Deere 7.6 litre engine, which John Deere originally claimed was "…loaded with reliable features…" These features included wet cylinder sleeves, seven main bearings and a dynamically, statically-balanced forged steel crank shaft. Another feature ➡

The original 55 series featured awkward steps and a bonnet-mounted exhaust which hindered visibility.

The long prominent bonnet with built-in work lights gives an aggressive look. The 55 series boasts American muscle.

Finding a late 55 series is proving very difficult, but they do appear, such as this example, seen at the Cheffins machinery sale.

The massive 7.6-litre engine provided as much as 1010Nm of torque and had a distinctive bark. The oil filter was also repositioned on later models to make oil changes quicker.

pointed out by the company was "Wedge-shaped" connecting rods, as their unique shape gives the underside of the piston pin a wider breadth to increase load-carrying area of the piston. Improvements over the 50 series included larger ports and valves which gave 20 per cent more air flow. This, together with a special domed combustion chamber, gave higher air-to-fuel ratios which in turn provided greater power and fuel efficiency. A further increase in torque was achieved by improving the turbo turbine and increasing the compressor efficiency – a viscous fan also reduced power-loss. The six-cylinder lump was both turbocharged and after-cooled to produce 190hp on the 4755 and 228hp on the 4955. This equated to a massive 178hp and 203hp respectively at the PTO, ideal for big square baling. The 115.9mm bore wasn't too oversized, but the stroke was fairly long at 120.6mm, which gave torque figures of a massive 820Nm and 1010Nm. The oil filter was conveniently repositioned allowing easier oil changes on later models from 1992 onwards.

Also they benefited from improved visibility, gained when the exhaust stack was moved up alongside the cab B post and the air pre-cleaner positioned under the bonnet. The fuel tank could swallow an enormous 386 litres in these larger two tractors, but the fuel filler position on top of the bonnet at the front wasn't the easiest to get at. Engines aren't usually a problem; some might suffer cooling problems from the failing of one of the three thermostats. Check the cooling system for signs of pressurising, as head gaskets could be an issue, especially where liners sometimes come free and eat the gasket away. These tractors certainly retain the noticeable Deere 'bark' of a power hungry tractor

GEARBOX
The transmission was a 15-speed PowerShift, which offered 15 forward and 4 reverse speeds of which eight of the speeds were between four and 12 kph in the primary tillage range. Speed changes

were 15 per cent when changing up, and only 13 per cent when down, which means power was never lost. Top speed was, sadly, no more than 19mph, so the tractor shouldn't be considered when a lot of road work is involved. You could shift into reverse from any forward speed without clutching and a single lever gives all speeds with no range changing. The layout means that the tractor was very easy to operate and could be picked up quickly by anyone. Check that all the gears change relatively smoothly and every gear works under load – applying the brakes for example. Ensure the park-brake works, it can be as simple as a missing pin, but internal problems won't be cheap to fix.

REAR LINKAGE
The three-point linkage was extremely sturdy and gave high-lift capacities and also offered tremendous stability as the long wheelbase gave good weight distribution. Maximum lift capacity for the Category III linkage was 5,160kg

An 8.4-ton lift capacity was more than enough and the design could be considered as bomb-proof. Look out for ARM and Dromone hitches for trailer work.

Side-mounted exhaust appeared in 1992 along with a host of improvements to the design

The left of the dashboard housed the IntelliTrak monitoring system and on the right-side it showed an interesting digital dial for engine rpm, temperature and fuel levels.

The powershift transmission gave easy changes up and down, and in direction – some gears can be jumpy especially when the oil is cold.

throughout the whole lift range, and a substantial 8,250kg in the fully-raised position. A spring-loaded toggle switch located on the rear fender provided remote control of the linkage on later models which is worth finding. Linkage control was by a single depth control lever and a rocker switch to provide a quick in and out, the first electro-hydraulic control. Look-out for Dromone and ARM hydraulic rear pick-up hitches, the majority will have a standard drawbar. Check that the linkage works in both draft and position, as sometimes there can be control problems. Also, don't forget wear in the linkage as many tractors will have handled big mounted equipment and are likely to have play by now.

HYDRAULICS AND PTO
An eight-piston variable displacement pump supplied the Closed Centre hydraulic system which operated at 2,530 PSI and provided as much as 126 litres per minute. Two spools were standard, and three were optional and in most cases will often be

fitted. Flow was easy to set on each outlet with easy connection of pipes by a simple lever. The PTO engagement had automatic modulation which meant that no matter how the lever was engaged it always activated smoothly. Attaching a PTO shaft was easy, as you were able to turn the shaft by hand when the tractor was not running and the shield conveniently flipped up for better access. Sadly, both tractors gave only 1,000rpm speeds, usually all that was required for big tractors, but the smaller models in the range offered 540 rpm.

AXLES AND BRAKES
The front wheels gave a 50-degree turn with a caster angle of 13 degrees, allowing the front wheels to lean into the turn. This equated to a 5,400mm turning radius without the brakes, excellent for such a physically large machine. Check the front hub seals as these can be a time-consuming job to replace, and expensive if not done properly. Four-wheel drive was engaged by a toggle switch on

the dash and featured an 'automatic' mode. At speeds above 14 kph, the drive automatically disengages to avoid damage and it also re-engages when braking – providing safer stopping power for the eight-ton monster. Brakes were multiple-disc wet brakes which were the priority-fed, hydraulic power type. Front axles have been known to fail as they can't handle the power on the 4955, but this was in extreme cases and a careful check should reveal any problems.

Track rod ends are renowned for breaking and can commonly fail, although are not a major job to swap. But they are still an additional expense – so check for play. As with any tractor, the front axles pivot does wear, so check to see if it is eating into the front casting. Four-wheel drive clutches can slip, but it is awkward to test this unless in a field, though expect to pay around £5-600 to have it replaced. Brakes do wear-out in time and can need changing at around 5 to 6,000 hours with average use. ➡

Parts	4955
Engine Oil Filter	£17.25
Fuel Filter	£25.75
Hydraulic Filter	£29.25ea
Inner Air Filter	£26.99
Outer Air Filter	£48.99
Fan Belts	£34.75
Starter Motor	£301.29
Alternator	£237.09
Water Pump	£357.94
Hydraulic Pump	£1410.00
Exhaust Silencer (late)	£290.00
Exhaust Pipe (late)	£330.00
Mirror Glass	£22.25

(All retail prices excluding VAT from a John Deere dealer.)

John Deere's HydrasCushioned seat gave arm-chair comfort and was extremely luxurious - ensure it works correctly

Contacts

Ben Burgess
East Anglia
01603 628251
www.benburgess.co.uk

Cornthwaites
Preston, Lancs
01995 606969
www.cornthwaites.co.uk

Burden Brothers Agri
Isle of Sheppey, Kent
0195 880224
www.burdenbros.co.uk

J W Doubleday Ltd
Holbeach St. Johns, Lincs
01406 540293

www.jwdoubleday.co.uk
Farol Ltd
Oxfordshire
01844 278843
www.farol.co.uk

Masons
Newton Abbot
Devon
01626 852140
www.jamesmasonltd.co.uk

Rea Valley Tractors
Pontesbury, Shropshire
01743 790801
www.rea-valley-tractors.co.uk

How much

Model	Year From	Year To	N	1	2	3
4755	1988	1994	£54,453	£16,000	£12,500	£8,750
4955	1988	1994	£60,806	£17,000	£13,250	£9,250

(Guide – N: 1991 New Price, 1: Excellent condition with no faults, 2: Tidy condition and useable, 3: Rough condition with high hours.)

Specifications

Model	4755	4955
Engine Make	Deere	Deere
Engine Model	6466A	6466A
Max Engine Power (hp)	190	228
Max Power @ (rpm)	2200	2000
Max Torque (Nm)	820	1010
Max Torque @ (rpm)	1210	1210
Number of Cylinders	6TI	6TI
Displacement (cc)	7640	7640
Bore (mm)	115.8	115.8
Stroke (mm)	120.6	120.6
Fuel Tank Capacity (Litre)	386	386
Standard Transmission	15F x 4R Powershift	15F x 4R Powershift
Lift Capacity (kg)	8415	8415
Turning Radius 4wd (mm)	5400	5400
Length (mm)	4559	4559
Width (mm)	2485	2485
Standard Weight (kg)	8034	8124
Std. Tyre Size Front	16.9R30	16.9R30
Std. Tyre Size Back	20.8R42	20.8R42
Cab	SG2	SG2

CAB

The existing SG2 cab which was used in previous years on the 50 series was fitted to the 55s for its last-ever outing. Maximum noise levels were an amazing 76 db(A), one of the leaders in the '80s. A few improvements were incorporated into the older 50 series design, such as plough lights on each cab corner and extendable rear-view mirrors. Three awkward steps helped operators to enter the cab, but they were improved and updated in 1992 when they were repositioned with the addition of a useful hand rail.

The round fender work lights changed to the square variety. The SG2 was fitted with one door, which made up half of the curved front windscreen and removed the front 'A' corner posts. A unique design, only used by John Deere at the time, but it also created many enemies due to the poor access. This design meant that the door latching pillar was just off-centre of the bonnet, which along with the exhaust pipe and air

cleaner stack reduced forward visibility on earlier models. Later models had a side-mounted exhaust which improved the visibility considerably. John Deere's posture seat adjusted in five different ways, with HydraCushioned suspension operating at 21 bar to maintain seat height. A nitrogen-filled accumulator gave an excellent ride. The left of the dashboard housed the IntelliTrak monitoring system which provided digital display of engine rpm, PTO rpm, area covered, and distance travelled. The second half of the display on the right-side was way ahead of its time, showing an interesting digital dial for engine rpm, temperature and fuel levels. The dashboard also housed the PTO engagement lever on the left and handbrake to the right, thus making them conveniently close to hand. The gear, linkage and spool levers were found on the side console, all very accessible. And when you are driving in this winter's rain, two wipers keep the front screens clear, while a three-speed fan

and air-conditioning keeps temperatures constant. Check that the air-conditioning works and has been updated to R134a gas and fittings.

VERDICT

A 4755 and 4955 would be a good bet if you were looking for a classic piece of American muscle, with little to go wrong. These tractors can often reach 10,000 hours, needing little work to the engine or the rest of the machine. The resale values can be often quite high and can be a good investment for buyers. Many of these tractors still fetch between £10-20,000, starting at around £8-9,000 and rising – so that you can expect to pay about £18,000 for an immaculate low-houred 1994 4755 or 4955. However, if you are a "used" buyer, finding an immaculate machine could be a very difficult task, but most tractors are arable machines and should still look in a reasonable condition. As from previous experience in the States, John Deere has designed the tractors to weather well. ■

Blues and greens

These two makes are rarely seen together, says Chris McCullough

A Northern Ireland tractor collector, who is a huge Ford fan, has added quite a rare John Deere 2140 to his collection in a move that has astounded his closer tractor friends.

A few months ago Cyril Hunter from Irvinestown in County Fermanagh, Northern Ireland's Lake District, added a John Deere 2140 in immaculate condition to his growing 'blue' collection.

It is a 1984 version (with 8,073 hours accumulated by one owner from new) which he bought in the north of England simply because it was so clean and tidy.

Cyril said: "It's not often that such a clean example of the John Deere 2140 comes up for sale, especially a two-wheel drive version with front mudguards. I had

heard about it coming up for auction and viewed the tractor before securing it."

The 2140 was first introduced to Europe in early 1980 with the SG2 cab and in 1983, when a depression hit the European tractor market, John Deere introduced a low-profile version of it. The John Deere 2140 was built until 1987.

Originally though, the 2140 was manufactured in Mannheim, Germany, and fitted with a John Deere four-cylinder engine rated at 82 horsepower.

On Cyril's version even the cab interior is "like new. The clutch and brake pedals show little wear."

His tractor has been on a few road runs and certainly created a lot of attention, being a relatively rare model in Northern Ireland.

However, everything has a price and Cyril says a good offer might persuade him to sell.

Originally from the north of England, Cyril Hunter's John Deere 2140 is very tidy and a credit to its previous owner.

John Deere 6 cylinder Sixty-Ten Series 1997-2002

The 6000 series first arrived in 1992 and were a radical improvement over the 'classic' design of the previous 50 and 55 series fitted with SG2 cabs. The re-design was long-overdue and was welcomed by most customers. The six cylinder tractors arrived later in 1994, but they all received a major update in 1997 with the addition of '10' series. Howard Sherren looks at the developments and why these tractors have again been so desirable in recent years, often considered the best tractor to be built by John Deere to date.

The 6910S topped the '10' series at 150hp. It was launched in 2001 just before the '20' series arrived. The 6910 was one of the most popular models and was the top selling tractor of 1998.

The 115hp 6610 (seen here) and smaller 105hp 6510 were good all-rounders and were commonly found on livestock farms.

Many tidy examples of the 10 series such as this 6910 are appearing at auctions on the used market, but strong export demand has kept prices high.

The '10' series tractors were an improved 6000 series, featuring more power, new features and revised decals.

J ohn Deere revealed their full-frame modular design in the Autumn of 1992 when the four cylinder 6000 series appeared to replace the ageing 3350 and 3650 models. Built at John Deere Werke Mannheim, the biggest 6400 model gave 100hp and was soon joined the following year by the six cylinder variants, the 110hp 6600 and 120hp 6800. Later that year they were joined further by the new flagship model, the 130hp 6900 and after a smaller six cylinder version, the 100hp 6506. Come November 1997, the complete range was due an improvement package, so all were re-badged '10' series.

They featured more power, with new transmissions and could be specified with the new, unique triple link suspension (TLS) system. They made their European debut in November 1997 at the Agritechnica exhibition in Germany and the new features were designed to provide easier, more comfortable operation, thereby increasing work rates and productivity. There were eight original models in all, from 80 to 140hp, all based on the company's field-proven full-frame concept with modular transmission and long life Perma Clutch II. Improvements

included the new generation John Deere PowerTech 4.5 and 6.8 litre engines, which were specifically designed to meet the future USA and EU tractor emission regulations without any loss in performance.

The new PowerTech engines were available with electronic governing, depending on the choice of transmission.

TLS

John Deere's fully suspended front axle, called Triple Link Suspension (TLS) was an exclusive development on the 10 series. It was unlike any other design on the market as the suspension system was permanently engaged, providing 100mm of travel - 50mm in either direction. The axle was supported by two hydraulic cylinders mounted vertically onto the front of the tractor frame, and an axially mounted arm ran from the axle to the frame's central casting. The system was particularly effective when working at higher speeds, for example when cultivating, spreading or mowing. It was optionally available for all models from the 6110 to the 6910.

There was a wide choice of transmissions to choose from - the 16/16 30kph and 20/20 or 24/24 40kph PowrQuad versions had four powershift gears and a left or right hand

power reverser with neutral position, or the new 20/20 or 24/24 PowrQuad Plus 40kph transmission, with left hand power reverser, which provided push-button shifting within the PowrQuad range, using a single lever control along with speed matching.

AutoQuad had the same features as PowrQuad Plus, but also incorporated electronic fuel injection governing, cruise control and automatic gear shifting within the range. In the field, this meant that the transmission would shift automatically depending on engine rpm and load. PowrQuad Plus was optionally available across the range, while AutoQuad was only an option on all tractors from the 100hp 6310 model upwards.

The TechCenter cab offered a host of new features, including a choice of four seats, an optional suspended passenger seat and extra storage space. An improved air conditioning system, new Dual Gauge II instrumentation with additional warning signals and better diagnostics, and reduced noise levels of around 75 down to 72db(A).

POWERSHIFT

At the Royal Smithfield Show in November 1998 another transmission option was added to the line-up. The 6810 and 6910 ➡

The right-hand side panel opens to reveal the oil filter and bonnet release mechanism - to get at the 6.8 litre Deere engine.

On the left the fuel filter, oil dipstick and filler are hidden, the panels further forward are removable, to enable easier radiator cleaning.

The Triple Link Suspension system is highly sought after and will demand a premium price, it was standard on 50kph tractors.

Not many issues on the front axle, usual check for greasing and signs of play when jacked off the ground. This standard axle was joined by the now-renowned 'TLS' at the range's launch.

Lift capacities were excellent, ranging from 5.9 tons up to 7.5 tons on the 6810 and 6910.

now became available with a powershift transmission, and the 6910 power was increased to 140hp. This was the first time a tractor was offered with a full 18 speed powershift transmission on a tractor of that size. A single lever provided selection of the 18 forward or 7 reverse gears up to a top speed of 40kph. From September 1999, all the John Deere 6910 tractors increased in horsepower from 135hp to 140hp. The 6810 Powershift tractor cost £55,202, while the 6910 Powershift model was £59,654, while adding TLS was an extra £2807, but sadly this gearbox option was discontinued in May 2001.

SE

February 1999 saw some new basic-specification tractors launched, known as the 'SE' models they were ideal for stock farms who didn't require the higher specification of the Premium models. The range came with the 16/16 PowerQuad transmission in 30kph or 40kph versions and a right-hand power reverser with neutral position. The TechCenter cab had a new, brighter interior with a full length roof hatch, optional air conditioning and new, fully adjustable Super Comfort seat. The optional low profile cab brought the total height of the tractor down

from 2.6m to 2.5m when fitted with 16.9 R30 tyres. The six cylinder models included the 105hp 6510 SE and turbocharged 115hp 6610 SE, but were with a standard cab only and basic prices started at £33,745 for a 30kph 6510 2WD up to £40,892 for the 40k 6610 SE 4WD.

AUTOQUAD II

The new AutoQuad II transmission with Field Cruise electronic engine control arrived in November 1999, with a 50kph top speed provided from July 2000. The 50k tractors now feature true four-wheel braking, thanks to front brakes which gave a 25% increase in stopping power. TLS was updated by fitting a new low friction cylinder providing a better ride The system won the 2000 Gold Medal in the RASE Machinery Awards, sponsored by Lloyds TSB and according to the RASE's award announcement, "The John Deere triple link suspension (TLS) system for 6010 and 7010 Series tractors provided users with improved traction, greater driver comfort, safer high speed roadwork and less wear and damage to tyres and implements. The outcome was higher hourly output, with drivers prepared to work longer hours, and more accurate work, for example when spraying and beet topping.

BEST SELLER

It was revealed at the turn of the century that the 6910 was the best selling tractor of 1998, and four other 10 series were ranked in the European top 10. On this fact, Deere launched a new 6910 model, the 150hp 6910S. This machine fitted in between the existing 140hp 6910 and its larger brother, the 160hp 7710. The 6910S offered a 5hp boost for PTO work and transport at 1900rpm and came standard with AutoQuad II in 40 and 50kph versions. The first stepless transmissions known as 'AutoPowr' were officially launched in the UK and Ireland at the 2000 Royal Smithfield Show. The CVT unit allows the tractor driver to change speed from 50m/hr up to 40 or 50kph, independently of engine speed. It was based on four years of development work with the transmission manufacturer ZF and became available on the 6610, 6810 and 6910, which took the choice of transmissions to four.

AUTOPOWR

AutoPowr's hydro-mechanical gearbox took the tractor from zero to maximum speed, while a simple selector knob that could be set for three transmission modes - manual, economy and power - for optimum working efficiency. To operate the tractor,

Linkage turn-buckles were a bit awkward to use, but the push-out hydraulic hitch was required to see past the spool block.

Up to 4 spools were available and often one was devoted to just the hitch.

Access to the TechCenter cab was pretty unhindered, but the bottom of the door was a little tight though. Steps gather muck and debris, also the bottom step is vulnerable but can be replaced easily.

Inside the cab, cladding and plastic can take a beating thanks to excellent build quality. Seat covering wears well and most interiors will clean up like new.

Dashboard was very clear and simple - the design was used for a number of years on most of the range.

The side console of the PowrQuad remained similar to the previous 6000 series, everything was easily to hand.

the driver simply selected the maximum speed and direction of travel, then pressed the accelerator. In addition to the AutoPowr selector, a left-hand reverser on the steering column could set for forward or reverse, with a central 'power zero' position that prevented rolling of the tractor when stationary. The control lever had two ranges which could be infinitely adjusted, and the maximum speed was shown by a needle on speedometer.

These last models have become the most desirable, especially the 50kph versions which require the biggest premium. Production was phased out when the replacement '20' series arrived, supporting new tinwork and cab design.

USED MODELS
ENGINE

The 10 series used the 6.8 litre John Deere Powertech engines to provide between 105 and 150hp. The 6910S which topped the range featured a 150hp engine which generated up to 155 maximum horsepower for transport and PTO work. Almost all the engines were turbocharged apart from the 6510, which was naturally aspirated. The 105hp 6510 and 115hp 6610 were also available in an 'SE' version.

These didn't have the same high specification as the 'Premium' models. This reduced the cost and made them more affordable to livestock farms. A 106.5mm bore and 127mm stroke were similar and inline with the competition, but rated speeds were lower at around 2100 rpm for the 6810 and 6910. The engines featured optimum fuel consumptions ranging from 203 g/kWh on the 6610 to 206g/kWh on the 6910, the lack of a turbo on the 6510 meant consumption was 210 g/kWh. The 250 litre fuel tank unfortunately did not provide enough capacity for the 6910 when under heavy working conditions, while the 207 litres on the smaller machines wasn't too bad in normal operation. Common problems that occur include over-heating, mainly due to blocked radiators, as even a partial blockage will send the temperature high. The cooling system was always on its' limit and really required more capacity. AutoPowr models would always be hot and if the mechanical fuel pump was ever tampered with could cause extra heat. Check the flexi-pipe that joins the exhaust and manifold as it can often split. The 6910S tractors electronic Bosch VP44 fuel pump was often frowned upon as it was ahead of its time and had produced less performance in comparison to the

standard 6910, though the two valve engine was improved later on 20 series tractors. Fuel pumps in the tank can sometimes fail, but you will only find this out when it comes to servicing and it cannot be primed.

GEARBOX

As described previously, there were four transmission variants available on the range. Firstly the PowrQuad and PowrQuad Plus transmissions were a versatile all rounder which had been tried and tested on both the 6 and 7000 series in previous years. PowerQuad had five or six ranges with four powershift gears to give either 20 or 24 forward and reverse speeds. The powershift gears could be changed using the lever or gear stick mounted buttons and by a rocker switch mounted on the side console on 'Plus' models. The second transmission option available is the AutoQuad II, which offered all the features of the PowerQuad Plus but with automatic shifting and cruise control. The Auto mode enabled the gearbox to shift up and down according to the load on the tractor and the engine speed. An Eco mode also allowed shifts to be made at lower engine speeds. ➡

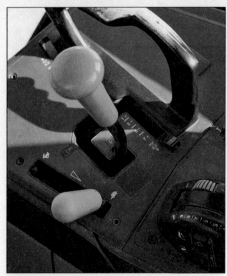

A few 6810 and 6910 models will have the PowrShift box seen here, not the best for shuttle work, but ideal for arable operations.

The AutoPowr transmission was launched just prior to the end of production and was controlled via this simple joystick and thumb-dial.

Finally John Deere offered the continuously variable AutoPowr transmission which gave a simple selection of any speed up to 40 or 50kph. Using the same principal as an automatic car, it was controlled by a single lever which can select up to two speeds in each direction. Adjustments to the selected maximum speed are made using a roller mounted on the end of the lever. All tractors featured the left hand Power Reverser which gave clutchless direction changes with a neutral position, and the AutoPowr option had an additional Park Lock position.

PowrQuad and AutoQuad gearboxes remain mainly trouble free and are very reliable, though some early AutoPowr transmissions have been found to cause problems. Most will now be sorted, but if a problem occurs a replacement transmission will cost in the region of £9,000, so very expensive if an error occurs. The tractors own error codes can pin-point any problems if they occur. It is best to avoid PowrShift models as they take a lot of power and feel gutless, and also watch out for some models that were specified with a 30kph top speed.

REAR LINKAGE

The category II/III linkage was mainly fitted with quick hitch, hook lower links, but fixed or telescopic link ends were available. Lift capacities range from 6900kg on the 6510, up to 7550kg on the 6910, plenty of capacity for all arable operations. Linkage control remained the same as the previous

range, but the slide lever still worked effectively and was a pleasure to use. The optional Headland Management System (HMS) was well worth finding, it reduced the amount of manual operations in the field, as much as 33% John Deere claimed. It automatically disengaged, PTO, 4WD etc when an implement was lifted and re-engaged when lowered back into work. The hydraulic telescopic hitch has always been an advantage on 6000 series Deeres and it was a must when trying to view the hitch from the cab thanks to the protruding spool block. Check the linkage rock-shaft and arms for worn bushes or play as lots of linkage work will cause plenty of wear here and it will get worse. Check the fender switches work as if they fail they will cost in the region of £30-40 to replace.

HYDRAULICS AND PTO

A pressure and flow compensating system (PFC) used a swash plate pump to provide up to 96 litres/min at 200bar. A maximum of four spool valves were a possibility, with lots of different configurations, including detent, float and kick-out functions. 540 and 1000 PTO speeds were available with an additional 540E on the 6610 upwards. The system was a high-speed and low torques system to reduce strain and a reversible PTO shaft was easy to swap and quick to change, an external PTO switch was also a useful feature. Though check the shaft for play in the carrier as the splines can round-off, losing drive. It will cost around £500 to have a new carrier fitted

to rectify this problem. Hydraulics either work or they don't, if the steering works it will likely be an electrical problem and if not a pump issue. Brake contamination can often damage a pump but they are usually trouble free, but error codes in the dash can pin-point the problems.

AXLES AND BRAKES

The ZF standard front axles gave very few problems Triple Link Suspension (TLS) was first seen on the 10 series and gave extra comfort and safety. The system consisted of 2 double acting cylinders and 3 accumulators to give 100mm of suspension travel. A 4.95m or 5.12m turning radius was as good as any similar tractor of this size, thanks to 12 degree caster and 52 degree steering angles. While the brakes consisted of oil cooled, self equalising and adjusting discs front and back. Brakes usually last between 4000 and 6000 hours, so check their effectiveness, as machines used solely at 50kph for transport work can eat brakes. When braking from a high speed, listen for a grating noise just before stopping, as this will be an indication that they need replacing. If a knocking noise can be heard from the TLS, it may be an indication the Panhard rod pins could be worn. The cast front fender brackets can break and cracks can often appear on 50kph models where the tyre resonance causes excessive vibration. Adjustable wheels can have lugs crack especially on high-speed tractors, check round the rims and try to buy tractors with solid centres if possible.

Specifications

Model	6510	6610	6810	6910	6910S
Engine make	Deere	Deere	Deere	Deere	Deere
Max Engine Power (hp)	105	115	125	140	150
Max Power @ (rpm)	2300	2300	2100	2100	2100
Max Torque (Nm)	430	471	561	606	630
Max Torque @ (rpm)	1495	1495	1365	1365	1500
Number of Cylinders	6	6T	6T	6T	6T
Displacement (cc)	6788	6788	6788	6788	6788
Bore (mm)	106.5	106.5	106.5	106.5	106.5
Stroke (mm)	127	127	127	127	127
Fuel Tank Capacity (Litre)	207	207	207	250	250
Standard Transmission	PowerQuad+ 20F x 20R	PowerQuad+ 20F x 20R	PowerQuad+ 20F x 20R	PowerQuad+ 20F x 20R	AutoQuadII 20F x 20R
Lift Capacity (kg)	5900	6660	7550	7550	7550
Turning Radius 4wd (mm)	4950	4950	5120	5120	5120
Length (mm)	4520	4520	4560	4560	4560
Width (mm)	2316	2316	2382	2382	2382
Standard Weight (kg)	4900	4900	4374	5590	5590
Std. Tyre Size Front	16.9 R24	16.9 R24	16.9 R28	16.9 R28	16.9 R28
Std. Tyre Size Back	18.4 R38	18.4 R38	18.4 R38	20.8 R38	20.8 R38
Cab	TechCenter	TechCenter	TechCenter	TechCenter	TechCenter

Prices

Model	Year From	Year To	N	1	2	3
6510	1997	2002	£42,685	£19,000	£15,000	£9,750
6610	1997	2002	£47,062	£21,500	£16,000	£10,250
6810	1997	2002	£50,692	£23,000	£17,750	£11,500
6910	1997	2002	£55,144	£25,500	£19,000	£12,750
6910S	2001	2002	£62,861	£26,500	£21,000	£14,000

(Guide – N: Last New Price, 1: Excellent condition with no faults, 2: Tidy condition and useable, 3: Rough condition with high hours.)

CAB

The 10 series TechCenter cab is primarily an updated version of the old 6000 series cab. The majority of the controls remain unchanged with a few improvements. The quality was still outstanding and was built to wear well and last. The cladding and plastic usually will clean up to look like new. Three steps led up to the flat floor, but they were good at collecting muck and the bottom step was a bit vulnerable. John Deere seat coverings last extremely well so should be in good order - ensure the air-seat lifts and lowers as it should. Tiltable steering column sometimes fails to lock in position when a gas damper fails, which costs in the region of £120 to replace.

The additional Left Hand Reverser shuttle was located underneath the steering wheel and should also be checked for functionality. Gauges were simple and consisted of an array of analogue dials and digital displays. Noise levels could reach 72 dB(A) when under load, 310 degree visibility and four speed blower were all welcomed improvements over the old SG2 design. A suspended passenger seat was an additional extra worth locating, though ensure the Grammar air seat operates as it should, as on 50kph models it has many axis of movement and can be pricey to replace.

VERDICT

The 10 series can certainly be described as the best tractor made by John Deere, thanks to a strong reliable, package which is very popular on the export market. Prices still remain high, with high houred, very rough tractors starting at £10,000 mark, while the last could see £25 to 26,000. Ensure to have a good drive, check with the dealer there are no error codes either through the dash or laptop and if everything seems to work you should be onto a good buy. The best tractor to buy and most desirable would be a 50kph PowrQuad Plus model 6910 and many dealers suggest a 6910 would be better than the 150hp 6910S version.

Models that have been available include a 1999 6910 with 40k and front weights with 5200 hours priced at £19,250, while a late registered 2002 6910 on an '04' plate, 50k Autopowr on 5500 hours was highest priced model at £24,500. Moving down to the 6810 model, a 1999 model with front linkage and 5000 hours on good back tyres was for sale at £19,750 and finally £17,000 buys a 4000 hour, 'V' registered 6610 and a Y registered model with 5000 hours stands at £19,500. ■

ACKNOWLEDGEMENTS

Steve Mitchell at ASM PR and Chris Willner at Rea Valley Tractors in Pontesbury for his technical help.

Contacts

Ben Burgess
East Anglia
01603 628251
www.benburgess.co.uk

Cornthwaites
Preston, Lancs
01995 606969
www.cornthwaites.co.uk

Burden Brothers Agri
Isle of Sheppey, Kent
0195 880224
www.burdenbros.co.uk

J W Doubleday Ltd
Holbeach St. Johns, Lincs
01406 540293
www.jwdoubleday.co.uk

Farol Ltd
Oxfordshire
01844 278843
www.farol.co.uk

Masons
Newton Abbot
Devon
01626 852140
www.jamesmasonltd.co.uk

Rea Valley Tractors
Pontesbury, Shropshire
01743 790801
www.rea-valley-tractors.co.uk

Parts	6910
Engine Oil Filter	£11.99
Fuel Filter	£19.50
Hydraulic Filter	£37.50
Inner Air Filter	£70.00
Outer Air Filter	£41.99
Fan Belt	£39.75
Starter Motor	£355.00
Alternator	£335.00
Water Pump	£165.00
Hydraulic Pump	£1510.00
Exhaust Silencer	£135.00
Exhaust Pipe	£230.00
Mirror Glass	£12.99

(All retail prices excluding VAT from a John Deere dealer.)

Comments

Likes
✓ Reliability and build quality
✓ Highly desirable and hold money
✓ Good capacity with plenty of options

Dislikes
✗ Limited cooling capacity
✗ Powershift tractors lack power
✗ Early AutoPowr tractor reliability

Buyer's Guide: John Deere
Seventy-Ten Series 1997-2003

Many John Deere users will class the 7710 and 7810 as one of the best tractors the company has manufactured. The dated design was finally replaced by the 20 series, the larger presence and extra technology of which was frowned upon by some 10 series owners. The last models to be produced have now become highly desirable. Howard Sherren investigates

he completely new 7000 series was launched in September 1992 with its smaller siblings, the 6000. Replacing the 55 series, the 7000s had a radical new design putting driver comforts to a new level, with stunning styling which created a stir. These ranges of tractors soon became known as among the most trusty available and were top-selling machines in the 150hp-200hp bracket.

Five years later John Deere revealed its '10' series update, introduced at the 1997 Royal Smithfield Show. The tractors featured increased horsepower and higher torque compared with the old models which they replaced. A new 8.1-litre PowerTech engine provided an extra 5hp for both the 160hp 7710 and the 175hp 7810. The 7600 did

receive the '10' status and was fitted with a 140hp, 6.8-litre PowerTech engine, but it was never imported into the UK. Many users found the 6900 and 6910 to be far more efficient machines, so there was little market for that particular model over here. Increased maximum power outputs of 166hp and 187hp were welcomed and in addition, each developed a massive torque rise of up to 50 per cent at the PTO.

An improved 19/7 Powershift transmission incorporated a computer control for smoother shifting under all load conditions. It also provided more usable speeds – 14 below 14kph – in the main field working ranges, and covered a total speed range from 1.6 to 40kph. Alternatively, a 20/20 40kph PowrQuad transmission was also available with the option of the new left-hand controlled power reverser for easier

loader work and faster headland turns. Extra standard features included the Headland Management System (HMS), a new foot throttle positioned more conveniently closer to the seat, shiftable PTO with a neutral position for easier implement hook-up, remote PTO control, and hitch dampening.

March 1999 saw the 7010 range fitted with the company's Triple-Link-Suspension (TLS) system, as featured on the smaller 6010 Series range that made its European debut at the Agritechnica exhibition in Germany in November 1997. Available as an option, the fully-suspended front axle was permanently engaged, providing 100mm of travel – 50 mm in either direction. This was designed to increase productivity by giving a more comfortable ride and better traction in the field, even when ploughing or using a front loader, as well as smoother

The 7010 series consisted of two models, the 160hp 7710 and 175hp 7810. Rear linkage capacity was originally a maximum of 7219 kg before exceeding the eight ton mark later on. Some operators struggled to lift heavy ploughs and became unimpressed.

performance on the road. An electronic level control monitored and constantly centralised the axle suspension for extra efficiency and safety in operation. The system was said to be particularly effective when working at higher speeds, for example, when cultivating, spreading or mowing. The tractor's hydraulic system was also improved by the new option of a factory-installed fourth and fifth Selective Control Valves (SCVs) with joystick controls increasing the versatility.

The last big update for the 7710 and 7810 was in September 2001 when they became available with the 50kph AutoQuad II or AutoPowr stepless transmissions. The AutoQuad II 50K package included Field Cruise electronic engine control, a trailer air-braking system and the new TLS II triple-link suspension system, which had been improved to provide smoother, softer, more consistent suspension performance. This transmission offered a true top speed of 50kph and was designed for customers who required higher transport speeds with lower overall noise, achieved as a result of reduced engine revs in the transmission's Eco/Auto modes.

A power boost feature generated extra power at transport speeds above 30kph, increasing rated engine performance at 2100rpm from 160 to 180hp on the 7710 and from 175 to 196hp on the 7810. These figures increased to 189 and 207hp respectively at 1900rpm. With AutoQuad II, shifting was automatic between four speeds in each of

five ranges, providing the operator with a total of 20 forward and reverse speeds, as well as speed matching between ranges. There was a choice of fully-automatic or manual push-button shifting from a single control lever.

AutoPowr allowed the tractor driver to change speed from 50m/hr up to 40 or 50kph, independently of engine speed. The hydro-mechanical gearbox takes the tractor from zero to maximum speed, while a simple selector knob could be set to four positions – off, PTO or one of the two economy modes for field and transport operations.

Drive on
To operate the tractor, the driver simply selects the maximum speed and direction of travel, then presses the accelerator. In addition to the AutoPowr selector, the cab controls include cruise control and the left-hand power reverser lever, mounted on the steering column. This could be set for forward or reverse, with a central 'power zero' position that prevents rolling of the tractor when stationary, as well as freewheeling, neutral and park positions. In place of the conventional right-hand controls, AutoPowr tractors also feature a single lever giving fully-independent, stepless speed control. This allows the driver to set two speed ranges for different applications and to change the set speeds easily on the move, using a built-in speed wheel, as well as shift between the two set

ranges whenever necessary. Finally, to meet the latest emission regulations, common rail fuel injection engines were installed from January 2003.

The 20 Series
Sadly, all good things come to end – a view held by many when the 20 Series was launched in 2004, sometime after the 6020 and 8020 models. For some customers, though, the update was well overdue and the new series brought the tractor in line with its competitors. However, those customers who were looking for a simple, rugged, manoeuvrable power-house were disappointed. The completely re-styled 20 series was a considerably bigger machine and had lost its small presence and dependability, but had gained improved cosmetics, features, technology and a better cab.

Time has yet to tell if these new tractors will gain the respect the 7710 and 7810 now enjoy.

Engine
The 7710 and 7810 both used a huge 8.1 litre PowerTech engine which featured a new piston design. This improved fuel and air mixing to boost the power and provided up to 50 per cent more torque rise. The 7710 pushed out 160hp, while the 7810 had 175 horses at hand. Maximum power reached 168 and 184hp respectively, not bad for the compact size of the tractor.

The 8.1 litre engine was considerably bigger than the other competitors in the power bracket of 150-175hp which used 7.6 ➡

The menacing look of the 7810 began to look dated by 2004 when it was replaced by the 20 series

Removable side panels were awkward to remove and hindered engine access

PTO and linkage controls were mounted on the rear fenders. Ensure that they function correctly

and 6.9 litre power lumps. The larger capacity of 8100cc, 116mm bore and stroke of 129mm also meant that the engines could handle a bit of tweaking. Many engines were prone to being opened up to a staggering 230hp or more without causing major problems. The ability to tempt a bit more power from the machines meant many could have been fiddled with, so it's best to locate an untouched model if reliability is a big concern. Dynomometer testing is a good tool to decide if a machine has been 'tuned', but the rest of the tractor was over-engineered, so it can stand up to the extra poke.

In order to check the engine over, the side-panels have to be removed, which can be tricky and a bit awkward. The fixed bonnet design was rectified on the later 20 series. As with any modern engine check for a service history, and look over the front pulley belt and its tensioner. Belt tensioners can eventually fail and a rattling is usually a good indication that mechanical attention is needed. The exhaust system should be checked for holes and cracks, brackets are commonly known to break and new exhaust tops can be bought when they burn through. The fuel tank at 344 litres provided adequate capacity for long working days in typical working conditions.

These engines were and are solid, rugged and have the ability to last 10,000 hours or more with no serious surgery.

Gearbox

With so many different options, 7010 buyers could choose the perfect gearbox to sort their operations. Over the lifespan of the range, the tractors had the choice of four different transmissions with options of a Left-Hand Shuttle Reverser (LHR) or creep box. Originally the first standard box was the 16F x 16R, or 20F x 20R PowrQuad which combined four or five ranges with a four speed powershift and shuttle. Also available at the launch was a 19F x 7R full Powershift unit, which was ideal for arable work, but best avoided when many directional changes were involved as there was no shuttle option. Control was via a single lever with a gate for forwards, reverse and a park-lock position.

Next to be offered was the 20 speed AutoQuad II which was similar to the PowrQuad, but with a number of new features. The powershift lever had been moved to buttons on the range lever, or

could be changed by a toggle switch on the side console. Automatic shifting with Power and Eco modes, cruise control and speed matching were other useful features. Finally, in September 2001, the launch took place of the 50kph AutoQuad II and infinitely variable AutoPowr transmissions. The AutoPowr single lever allowed you to move from 0-50k without gaps.

Two speed ranges were available and the maximum limit in each could be adjusted by a thumb wheel on the lever, and any speed changes were then made by moving the lever – an excellent idea which gave Fendt's Vario a run for its money. The gearbox was another very strong point for Deere in terms of reliability. (Today, just check for smooth shifts and that the shuttle works satisfactorily.) The LHR was known to fail on some models, which meant that the whole unit would need to be replaced.

If you are looking at an early model and the shift is possibly jerky, the software should be checked by a dealer and the latest versions installed.

Rear linkage and PTO

The CAT III rear linkage was well-built and certainly up to the job, giving a lift capacity of 7219kg originally and later 8150kg. The electro-hydraulic system had lower-link draft-sensing, with hitch dampening and external switches on the rear fenders. A few users found that the 7010 series wouldn't pick up heavy six-furrow ploughs in some cases, so always ensure that the tractor is up to the jobs you intend to use it for. Because of the heavy machinery they can lift, pivot and cross-shafts wear is common. Check the amount of play at each pivot and keep an eye on the cross-shaft as it can lead to thousands of pounds in repair bills.

Hydraulics

The pressure-and-flow hydraulic system with load-sensing gave a maximum pressure of 200 bar with a maximum flow of 100 litres per min. With up to five spools available with continuous, automatic or no detent positions, the 10 series was well suited to arable operations. Servicing is a very important part of the system, so ensure that the filters and oil have been regularly changed as pump life can be dramatically reduced. Generally the pump will last ages, thanks to a load-sensing, flow-on-demand system.

The spools are manually controlled which provides extra reliability, but do check for play in the levers and worn cables.

Axles and brakes

The 7710 and 7810 both use power brakes which are of the wet disc variety. The transmissions all have a Park-Lock and in addition to that there is a secondary hand-brake as well. 4WD braking engages at speeds less than 18 km/h and all 50k tractors have air brakes fitted as standard for extra safe braking. The Triple Link Suspension (TLS) was introduced in March 1999 and TLS II arrived in September 2001. It provided 100mm of travel and smoothes the ride considerably; a must when travelling

Four steep steps lead up to TechCentre cab; step condition often indicates how the tractor has been looked after.

Up to five spools could be specified, check for leaks and check the condition of the manual cables

Telescopic trailer hitch is a must when reversing to hook trailers. Look for wear on the hook as the tractors were often used with large trailers

Seat coverings are hard wearing, but air seat mechanisms should be assessed on higher-houred tractors

Digital dash is simple to use and reliable, push buttons provide all the vital information. Check the steering column tilt adjustment locks into position.

Front linkage and PTO were a common addition to the 10 series, as they were powerful and compact – ideal for front and rear mowers.

The Left-Hand Reverser (LHR) seen here was fitted to PowrQuad and AutoQuad transmissions as an option, it can fail.

LHR on the last tractors with AutoPowr had a 'park' position and a 'PowerZero' position which holds the transmission in position to stop it rolling.

The side console of a Powrshift model, the simple single lever controls gears, direction and the park-lock.

A later version of the PowrQuad transmission featuring the left-hand reverser.

Specifications

Model	7710	7810
Engine make	JD Powertech	JD Powertech
Engine Power (hp)	160	175
Max Power (hp)	166	187
Max Power @ (rpm)	2100	2100
Max Torque (Nm)	802	865
Max Torque @ (rpm)	1400	1400
Number of Cylinders	6T	6T
Displacement (cc)	8100	8100
Bore (mm)	116	116
Stroke (mm)	129	129
Fuel Tank Capacity (Litre)	344	344
Standard Transmission	20F x 20R PowrQuad	20F x 20R PowrQuad
Lift Capacity (kg)	7219	7219
Turning Radius 4wd (mm)	5130	5130
Length (mm)	4755	4755
Width (mm)	2438	2438
Standard Weight (kg)	6580	6620
Std. Tyre Size Front	16.9 R30	16.9 R30
Std. Tyre Size Back	20.8 R42	20.8 R42
Cab	TechCenter	TechCenter

Prices

Model	Year From	Year To	N	1	2	3
7710	1997	2003	£67,264	£35,000	£24,500	£13,500
7810	1997	2003	£71,305	£38,000	£27,000	£14,250

(Guide – N: Last New Price, 1: Excellent condition with no faults, 2: Tidy condition and usable, 3: Rough condition with high hours.)

50k. Check the pivots of both the suspended and non-suspended axles, as they will undoubtedly see wear and tear if not regularly maintained. The later AutoPowr and AutoQuad tractors are fitted with a full locking differential, as opposed to a limited slip in the earlier machines.

Check for clean oil here and assess any leaking hubs. The turning circle was excellent at 5.1m, thanks to its 52 degree steering and 13 degree caster angle.

Cab

Four steep steps lead up into John Deere's TechCenter cab, a fair hike but it gives a dominant driving position. Check the bottom steps for damage; replacements are available at a cost, but are easy to replace. Slim-line cab pillars and large glass area gave excellent views. A huge great armchair of a seat was both practical and comfortable, featuring four-way seat attenuation, and a rocker switch on the armrest provided adjustment of the height. The seat coverings tended to last extremely well and so shouldn't show any tears even with high hours on the clock. The seat mechanism and pump are – sadly – weak points. Check the seat pumps to the top and listen; wear can be

assessed by the amount of noise emitted on higher-houred tractors.

As with any John Deere cab, the cladding cleans up well and the build quality means that there should be little damage. It should be a good indication of the previous history if panels are broken and the foam ripped. Air-conditioning has known to be poor, so ensure that it cools efficiently otherwise a re-gas maybe required.

All-digital dash was both simple and reliable; a selection of push buttons provided detailed information and changed settings. The steering column was adjusted by a lever under the dash, the damper system was also

known to fail – meaning that the steering column would drop and not lock into place. These are expensive to replace, so check that you can lock it properly. Finally, foot throttle location and design was changed on numerous occasions, but the gear levers and side console was all located perfectly and very little stretching was required.

Verdict

If you are looking for a reliable, manoeuvrable power house, the 7010 series could be ideal. Suited to all farming types, the 7710 and 7810 have various different transmission options to suit every operation. Choose the right tractor carefully, as models which haven't been regularly serviced and maintained lead to very big repairs. Also ensure the engine hasn't been 'opened up' to achieve more power. Later common rail engines are a safer bet as they cannot be tampered with.

The most desirable tractors are the last 50k AutoQuad and AutoPowr machines which change hands for £30 to £40,000 depending on the hours. The majority of tractors will fall around the £25,000 mark, with some of the earliest, high-houred tractors as little as £15,000. ∎

John Deere 8010 Series 1999-2002

In October of 1994 the legendary new range of flagship tractors arrived, ranging from the 185hp 8100 up to the 260hp 8400. Howard Sherren looks at the later and improved 8010 tractors introduced from 1999.

J ohn Deere claimed its 8000 tractors to be: 'Patented tractors that push out the boundaries of power', so when launched on October of 1994 they were a radical advancement in terms of design and productivity. They were the first to have their design patented, which mainly referred to the integrated chassis design where the in-line, six-cylinder turbocharged engine had been moved forward by 44in, and raised by 10in, to a position over the front axle. This helped to achieve a stable 40/60 weight split when adding implements and ballast. Also the tapered wasp-waist hood allowed unprecedented forward visibility; and high horsepower performance can be combined with the

manoeuvrability of a much smaller tractor. The range was completely new and not just an updated design and the range line-up consisted of the 185hp 8100, 210hp 8200, 230hp 8300 and 260hp 8400.

Thanks to the tapered chassis design, the front wheels could pivot under the tractor frame, tucking in neatly underneath the engine allowing a turning radius of less than 5.2m at a 60" track, which also applied when large tyres and front fenders were fitted. An all-new 16-forward and five-reverse speed Powershift transmission used minimal gear meshes to maximise power efficiency in the field and provided speeds from 1.4 to almost 24mph without clutching, in 0.5mph increments in the working range.

Another major development was the CommandView cab which provided 65

per cent more interior space and nearly 6m^2 of tinted glass with a one-piece front windscreen offering an unobstructed view. Comfort-wise the air-cushioned seat was centred in the cab to improve the view both forwards and backwards, whilst the telescopic steering column had a memory setting so that it always returns to the same position, no matter how many times the driver gets in and out.

The revolutionary CommandARM armrest control module to the driver's right which swivels around with the seat kept all the controls at finger-tip reach. The secondary monitoring and instrumentation systems were located on a side panel, also to the right of the driver. An exclusive TouchSet hydraulic control panel allowed the driver to programme the SCVs to deliver precise implement response.

The 8010 series was an update for the original 8000 series that appeared in 1994. A tracked version was also available, but less common here in Britain.

The flagship 8410 model gave 270 horses from Deere's 8.1-litre power plant.

A tracked version of the 8000 arrived in 1997 and continued in the 8010 range.

Tracks for the home market

John Deere's 8000T tracked tractors first arrived in the Autumn of 1997 and retained all the proven features of the award-winning wheeled models, and Deere was the first manufacturer to offer customers a choice of tracks or tyres in this power class.

The rubber tracks used a friction drive system with hydrostatic differential steering, which was electronically controlled and speed-sensitive. A track-tensioning cylinder connected to the front idler wheel maintained pressure on the track by pushing the front idler forward, to ensure sufficient friction between the track and the rear drive wheel. Sets of three mid rollers support the centre of each track and kept them in contact with the ground over their full length. If track tension dropped due to loss of pressure in the tensioning cylinder,

a system warning light came on, and the tracks were simply re-tensioned using the tractor hydraulics.

Tread widths could be adjusted easily between 1.72m and 2.23m on the standard 60cm (24in) wide tracks. The optional 40cm (16in) wide tracks offered tread adjustments from 1.52m to 2.23m. Track alignment is also straightforward via the front idler. The 16 forward, four reverse PowerShift transmission was limited to 30kph, unlike their wheeled counterparts.

8010 Update

Keeping the patented original design, in November 1999 the new 8010s had a host of features which included: Automatic PowerShift Transmission (APS) and Implement Management System (IMS) as standard, both of which were exclusive

to John Deere, in addition to Hitch Slip Command (HSC).

"These machines were developed with the help of valuable farmer feedback and in response to customer demand for simpler tractor operations plus extra power and productivity," says John Deere Limited tractor Product Manager Gordon Day. "We have done more than simply increase the horsepower – the 8010 Series range has been specifically designed to provide farmers with more solutions to their individual operating needs, both in the field and on the road."

Based on the 16 forward, five reverse speed transmission, Automatic PowerShift eliminated the need to shift gears in the field or on the road, and was the first of its kind to function in both working and transport speed ranges. The APS controls ➡

The 10 series received additional front lights as well as larger and more prominent decals.

Engines can go on and on, though if it overheats there will probably be a problem with the water pump where the pump impeller comes adrift.

Engines can go on and on, though if it overheats there will probably be a problem with the water pump where the pump impeller comes adrift.

At 215hp the 8210 was good all-rounder machine; all tractors in the 8010 series were fitted with the same engine, unlike the first of the 8000s.

were incorporated on the cab's vehicle monitor and CommandARM armrest panel. Once the driver had set the maximum gear required, in APS mode the tractor would not shift above this selected gear, but would automatically shift down or up below this maximum level if one or more of the inputs required it to do so. The new Implement Management System was the first such system to manage both tractor and implement functions, providing the ultimate in control and ease of operation when carrying out consistent, repetitive tasks. IMS let the driver control up to 12 separate functions simultaneously, in any order or combination, at the touch of a switch.

In addition, a new hitch dampening feature hydraulically controlled the tractor three-point hitch to reduce shock loads and improve the ride when transporting mounted implements. Up in the cab an improved Comfort Command seat and improved air conditioning and heating system were the main benefits

A further optional package offered ClimaTrak automatic temperature control, and a delayed lighting system for use when leaving the cab at night. Hydraulic pump capacity had been increased by 11 per cent, the PTO brake engagement was also improved, and there was a new automatic shutdown feature. These additional features make the 10 series a favourable buy over the originals as we find out…

Engine

John Deere opted for both 7.6 litre and 8.1 litre engines on the original 8000 series, however all the 8010s came with the reliable PowerTech high-torque 8.1-litre engines with the exclusive Field Cruise electronic engine control which could generate up to 10 per cent extra PTO power when it was needed most. This also helped to keep to the latest emission levels and reduce fuel consumption.

Maximum power outputs of the six-cylinder, turbocharged and air-to-air aftercooled engine were 200, 227, 250 and 283hp on the flagship 8410. A bore of just under 116mm and stroke of just under 129mm meant the engines had plenty of grunt behind them, and torque figures ranged from 900Nm on the 8210 increasing to 1261Nm on the 8410. A 511-litre fuel tank was 125 litres bigger than the previous 55 series allowing the more powerful engines to go on for longer before those all-important fill-ups. As these tractors were ➡

The beefy backend could handle 8 tonnes on the smaller two models, whilst the 8310 and 8410 hoisted 9 tonnes.

mainly intended for arable use, the hours won't be that colossal yet, with many still under 5,000 hours.

There are many just about into five figures though and they have proved extremely reliable, with an external overhaul often recommended around the 10,000-hour mark. A few tractors have had issues with over-heating which was due to the water pump impeller coming adrift, but this was a simple repair. Look for signs of regular servicing as with any engine this will help to lengthen the engine's life and check round the exhaust system as holes can burn though on bends and elbows.

Gearbox

The 8010 series came with the same 16-speed Powrshift of the previous 8000s, but it featured Automatic PowrShift system which matched working speed to operating load. This improved efficiency, reduced fuel consumption and maximised power.

The basic 16 forward and 5 reverse transmission was controlled by a small joystick which had three notches, a park brake and forward and reverse ranges. By moving the lever into each gate, it was sprung loaded so just tapping forward or back it would change up and down gears.

The new Comfort Command seat welcomed operators with many more adjustments – check that it pumps up ok.

A good set of steps gave excellent access to the TechCenter cab. The bottom steps were prone to being damaged if set outwards.

If held in one position it will skip gears and would reach a maximum speed of 38.16kph in top gear. The gearbox again was trouble-free as earlier problems on the previous range were cured by a series of updates. Carry out your usual checks by getting the tractor backend oil hot and monitoring each gear and the way it changes. Any rough direction changes or jumpy changes mean the powershift packs are likely to be getting worn. Packs wear in time and will often depend on how the tractor has been driven and it's difficult to say when they will fail.

Rear linkage

At the rear the 8110 and 8210 can hoist 8 tonnes, and the 8310 and 8410 even more at 9 tonnes. The tractors also came with the new Hitch Slip Command which claimed to optimise pull. The system allowed the driver to set the amount of wheel slip they wanted in work and then the hitch would raise or lower automatically to maintain this.

Also the linkage now featured a dampening system for transporting heavy, fully-mounted implements. Linkage controls were typical of Deere, a sliding depth control, and dials for sensitivity, raise height and rate of drop.

With the additional features on the 8010s, they made a favourable buy over the older series. Though as with many Deeres, they did suffer from cross-shaft wear, so check the bushes and splines for play by lifting it manually and looking for movement. If this is not rectified it could lead to an expensive repair.

Look-out for Dromone hydraulic pick-up hitches if one is required, they may not be up to the job, but can be a handy addition for trailer work.

Hydraulics and PTO

The hydraulics were that of a closed centre, pressure/flow compensated system which had a gear pump that provided 127 litres

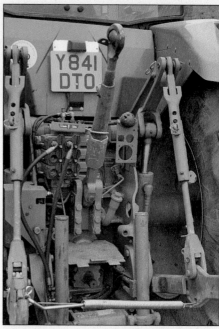

Look-out for cross-shaft bearing and spline wear, also a pick-up hitch was useful but not the best design and sometimes not up to the job.

a minute at 200 bar. The pump provided as much as 114 litres to the three standard spool valves. Many tractors were fitted with the extra 4th spool valve and 5th was also available. The spools were controlled by finger-tip switches on the CommandARM console where they gave extend, neutral, retract, float and timed detent positions. In addition they also offered a 'feather' control, so the further you push the more oil was delivered. The TouchSet hydraulics were the best on the market and extremely advanced which allowed you to digitally set the flow and timers for each hydraulic spool at the touch of a button or dial. Once mastered the feature could be extremely productive. One 45mm 1,000rpm PTO shaft was standard and a 540/1,000rpm set-up was offered as an option for light-use.

It was controlled by a push-up flip switch next to the linkage control. Very little to go wrong here; ensure that all the features function correctly and that the right number of spools or PTO speeds are fitted.

Axles and brakes

The front axle provided some excellent turning angles and the waisted frame enabled bigger tyres to be fitted without hindering manoeuvrability. A 5.25m ➡

Wasp-like bonnet helped to improve the turning circle and to fit bigger front wheels. Check the springs on the pivoting front fenders.

Model	Year From	Year To	N	1	2	3
8110	1999	2002	£73,180	£37,000	£31,000	£18,000
8210	1999	2002	£78,054	£39,250	£33,000	£19,250
8310	1999	2002	£85,614	£41,250	£34,500	£20,000
8410	1999	2002	£91,207	£35,500	£35,500	£21,750

(Guide – N: Last New Price, 1: Excellent condition with no faults, 2: Tidy condition and usable, 3: Rough condition with high hours.)

Parts	4955
Engine Oil Filter.	£19.75
Fuel Filter	£29.75
Hydraulic Filter	£105.00
Inner Air Filter	£33.50
Outer Air Filter	£73.00
Fan Belt	£38.50
Starter Motor	£320.94
Alternator 140A	£515.00
Water Pump	£270.00
Hydraulic Pump	£1290.00
Exhaust Silencer	£260.00
Exhaust Pipe	£65.00
Mirror Glass	£16.75

(All retail prices excluding VAT from a John Deere dealer.)

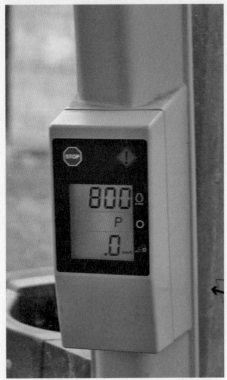

The side console was an array of digital displays, switches and knobs. Many unused by novice drivers but take time to check that everything works and what they do.

Engine speed, gears and forward speed were displayed by the information panel on the right-hand pillar.

TouchSet hydraulics gave finger-tip adjustment of flow rate and timers of spool valves – an advanced system ahead of the competition.

Front suspension wasn't available on the range as they were designed for the field and not transport. Some front axles couldn't take shock loads on the largest models so assess for damage.

turning radius was excellent and the front fenders feature a spring to absorb shocks and pivot slightly. The universal joints did not require servicing and there were only eight grease points which kept maintenance to a minimum.

Ensure that the tractor has had plenty of front ballast as some dealers have reported problems where the power cannot be transmitted to the ground and end up shock-loading the axle. Also if the locking rack on the rear bar-axle has come loose at any stage it would be difficult to keep tight again, so check this area. The power brakes were the enormous wet disc variety and shouldn't pose any problems. Tracks were also available although less common in the United TraderKingdom, but check track, idler and drive wheel condition. But the tracks should be the deciding factor and the biggest cost to replace.

Cab

Described as 'Outstanding', the TechCenter or CommandView cab was a considerable improvement over the old SG2 design. Large and extremely well-positioned steps led up to the operator platform. The bottom step could be moved to allow the fitment of larger front wheels and make access easier, but it

did mean the steps were more vulnerable if modified. The large single door gave plenty of space to enter the working environment and 8010 series drivers were welcomed by the new ComfortCommand seat offering even more adjustments.

The integrated CommandARM control centre ensured that all the controls moved with you when you turned the seat to the side. Looking forward there was no dashboard to hinder the unusual wasp-like bonnet which sprouted from the steering column. A display on the right cab pillar provided the vital information such as engine rpm, speed and gears.

A passenger seat was an optional extra so look out for this, in addition to the Field Office to the left of the cab. Check the air-conditioning function, as with no side windows it must be up to scratch, and also ensure that the electric mirror on the right-hand side works as it is vulnerable to being knocked and a pain to adjust manually.

Verdict

The 8010 series receives a status similar to the rest of the 10 series, such as the 6010 and 7010 series. A bomb-proof design with a host of excellent features has kept resale prices and export demand high. The tractors aren't

suited to roadwork, but come into their own in the field and still make a perfect buy for arable farms. Although there are no major problems, just check the points mentioned in the guide, especially the linkage cross-shaft. These advanced tractors still have a demand on the used market, especially in the rest of Europe which keep prices extremely high. Prices start around the £20,000 mark for rough models, with good examples at about £30,000. Late mint tractors will sell at up to £40,000 or more.

Acknowledgements

Steve Mitchell at ASM PR, Jimmy Lockhart at Ben Burgess Ltd and Chris Wilner at Rea Valley Tractors for their technical help. ∎

Comments
Likes
✓ Steering lock
✓ Automatic PowerShift (APS)
✓ TouchSet hydraulics

Dislikes
✗ Linkage cross-shaft bushes
✗ Not suited for transport
✗ Export demand

An aerial view of John Deere Limited UK & Ireland showing the site at Langer, Nottinghamshire.

John Deere Limited UK & Ireland 1915-2010

Since 1966, and from very small beginnings, John Deere Limited has grown to be one of the biggest suppliers of tractors and agricultural machinery to British and Irish farmers, with a reputation for product quality and performance. Regular staff and dealer training courses, and continuing investment in new products and manufacturing systems, ensure that John Deere is able to provide the most advanced and reliable products, backed by efficient and knowledgeable service and customer support. In 2008 the company increased its number one status in the UK to 30.2 percent, that's 5,613units (total units 18,564). Incidentally JD was also number one in its European manufacturing hub of Germany in 2009 with 19.3 percent 5,674 units (total units 29,465).

THE EARLY DAYS
The 25hp Waterloo Boy Gas Engine Co's tractor was sold in the UK under the Overtime banner, assembled at Hounslow, London, over 3,000 were sold during the 1914-18 war. They were a well liked reliable tractor that did the job well; this company was to be taken over by John Deere on 14th March 1918.

In the latter half of the 1930's, people like FA Standen and Jack Olding sold John Deere's rowcrop A and B's and standard examples of the same and styled D and some G's. They became particularly successful in East Anglia and other parts of the United Kingdom during Lend Lease.

After plans to set up a manufacturing site near Glasgow, Scotland in the 1950s things became frustrated for the company. The American parent Deere & Company purchased the Heinrich Lanz factory in Mannheim, West Germany, which in 1956 was very run down. It remains today the most modern tractor factory in Europe and is Deere's main European manufacturing base.

ESTABLISHED 1966
As the marketing company for the UK and Ireland, John Deere Limited commenced trading from its present day headquarters at Langar, near Nottingham, in January 1966 a former World War Two base. The main product line at this time consisted of the 710, 4020, 5010 and 5020 tractors, ploughs, cultivators, disc harrows and the 530 and 630 combines. Of the original dealers who, for a short time, sold large tractors imported from the USA through a franchise operation in the early 1960s, continued with the new company, two are still John Deere dealers today, and owned by the same families. They are Ben Burgess in Norwich, Norfolk, and P.Tuckwell at Worlingworth in Suffolk.

MARKET LEADERSHIP
Over the last four and a half decades, while the home tractor market has more than halved and many well known names have disappeared, John Deere's market share has risen from almost nothing to a position of market leadership. The company's share of the combine market has also risen. Annual sales have increased over 100 fold, from under £1.5 million to more than £150 million, during this time. According to the American Journal Business Week, John Deere spends more on Research and Development, than any other farm machinery company. In 1972, John Deere Limited was awarded the Royal Warrant as suppliers of agricultural equipment to Her Majesty The Queen

JOHN DEERE LTD TODAY
John Deere's new two storey office premises and training centre were officially opened in May 1998 by HRH The Princess Royal. They cover a total of 42,000ft2, and comprises state of the art training and workshop facilities plus modern, air conditioned offices and a stylish staff restaurant for the company's 105 employees.

The training centre replaces the company's previous facilities at Bingham. Together with the existing premises, the new building allows John Deere Limited to have all its office, training, workshop and parts storage facilities on one site, for the first time since the company was established at Langar. The UK headquarters have achieved certification to ISO 9002, the most comprehensive quality standards attainable by any business.

In 2000, the John Deere front axle suspension system for four-wheel drive tractors won the Gold Medal in the RASE machinery awards (the first time that John Deere Ltd has received a Gold Medal in this scheme).

All John Deere's dealers are connected by computer to the company's worldwide parts network, by the Distribution Network System (DNS). This provides instant information on parts availability, day or night, with orders shipped from anywhere in the world within 24 hours and overnight or even same day delivery on the UK mainland. ∎

The 20 Series had a few problems on release but many models have been subjected to a number of upgrades It's a good idea to check with the local JD dealer whether the work has been done.

John Deere 6020 Series

Launched in 2001, John Deere's 6020 series was the second update to their 6000 series, which was first seen back in 1993. Featuring all new styling and features, the 20 series was something different to the 10 series update. The tractors sold in great numbers and the 150hp 6920 is still one of the best sellers. Howard Sherren reviews the 6 cylinder 6020 series and finds out the pros and cons of the 6920.

ENGINE

The 20 series uses 6.8 litre John Deere Powertech engines to provide between 110 and 160hp. The 6920S which tops the range features a 160hp engine which generates up to 166 maximum horsepower for transport and PTO work. Almost all the engines are turbocharged apart from the 6520, which is naturally aspirated. The 115hp 6520 and 125hp 6620 are also available in an SE version, which did not have the same high specification as the 'Premium' models. This reduced the cost and made them more affordable to livestock farms. A 106.5mm and 127mm stroke bore which was similar to the competition, but rated speeds were lower at around 2100 rpm. The engines feature a new charge air cooler which reduces air intake temperature. This provides better combustion and fuel efficiency, which combined with the

Dual Temperature Cooling system (DTC) provides high torque and low emissions. Due to emissions, early tractors had two valve engines, while the later machines from 2003 onwards had four valves. These later type engines were found to be a lot thirstier when not undertaking hard work. The 250 litre fuel tank unfortunately did not provide enough capacity for the 20 series when under heavy working conditions. Servicing was extended to 500 hours, which helps save money on consumables.

Engines remain very reliable and very few problems have been reported.

GEARBOX

Three transmissions were available on the range. Firstly the PowerQuad Plus transmission is a versatile all rounder which has been tried and tested on both the 6 and 7000 series in previous years. PowerQuad has five or six ranges with four powershift gears to give either 20 or 24 forward and reverse gears.

The 20 series was found to be a very reliable and versatile machine that would suit almost any application.

Launched in 2001, the 6020 series became a huge success for Deere. The flagship 160hp 6920S seen here has become a highly desirable second hand buy.

PARTS FOR THE 6920

Engine Oil Filter	£9.99
Fuel Filter	£17.50/14.25
Hydraulic Filter	£31.99
Transmission Filter	£42.75
Air Filter Inner	£22.25
Air Filter Outer	£50.00
Fan Belt (maximum)	£52.00
Starter Motor	£305.00
Alternator	£260.00
Water Pump	£490.00
Hydraulic Pump	£1330.00
Exhaust Pipe	£145.00
Exhaust Silencer	£205.00
Mirror Glass	£11.75

(All approximate RRP prices excluding VAT. Depending on specification.)

The powershift gears can be changed using the gear stick mounted buttons or by a rocker switch mounted on the side console. The second transmission option available is the AutoQuad 2, which offered all the features of the PowerQuad Plus but with automatic shifting and cruise control. The Auto mode enables the gearbox to shift up and down according to the load on the tractor and the engine speed. An Eco mode also allows shifts to be made at lower engine speeds. Finally John Deere offered the continuously variable AutoPowr transmission which offers a simple selection of any speed up to 40 or 50kph. Using the same principal as an automatic car, it is controlled by a single lever which can select up to two speeds in each direction. Adjustments to the selected maximum speed are made using a roller mounted on the end of the lever. All tractors feature the left hand Power Reverser which gives clutchless direction changes with a neutral position, and the

AutoPowr option has a Park Lock position.

Gearboxes remain mainly trouble free and are very reliable. Some AutoPowr transmissions have been found to cause problems so check to see if they function correctly.

REAR LINKAGE

The category II/III linkage is mainly fitted with quick hitch, hook lower links, but fixed or telescopic link ends were available. Lift capacities range from 6750kg on the 6520, up to 8565kg on the 6920, plenty of capacity for all arable operations. Linkage control remains the same as the previous range, but the slide lever still works effectively and is a pleasure to use. When in transport position, automatic hitch dampening gives a smoother ride. Limited linkage movement means extra adjustment is always needed on the hitch rods when using different implements. The hydraulic telescopic hitch has always been an advantage on 6000 series Deeres and it is a

must when trying to view the hitch from the cab. The linkage stabiliser bars work well and are praised by most users, but they do have a tendency to not lock in some situations.

HYDRAULICS

A pressure and flow compensating system (PFC) used a swash plate pump to provide up to 96 litres/min at 200bar. A number of different control valves were available on the machines and a maximum of four spool valves is a possibility. 540 and 1000 PTO speeds are available with an additional 540E on the larger three tractors. A reversible PTO shaft is easy to swap and quick to change.

AXLES AND BRAKES

John Deere's Triple Link Suspension (TLS II) was continued on the 20 series and gave extra comfort and safety. The system consists of 2 double acting cylinders and 3 accumulators to give 100mm of suspension ➡

Specifications

Model	6520	6620	6820	6920	6920S
Engine Power (hp)	110	125	135	150	160
Max Power @ (rpm)	2300	2300	2100	2100	2100
Max Torque @ (rpm)	1495	1495	1365	1365	1365
Number of Cylinders	6	6T	6T	6T	6T
Displacement (cc)	6788	6788	6788	6788	6788
Bore (mm)	106.5	106.5	106.5	106.5	106.5
Stroke (mm)	127	127	127	127	127
Fuel Tank Capacity (Litre)	207	207	250	250	250
Standard Transmission	PQ Plus 24/24	PQ Plus 24/24	PQ Plus 20/20	PQ Plus 20/20	AutoQuad2 20/20
Lift Capacity (kg)	6750	7565	8565	8565	8565
Turning Radius 4wd (mm)	5120	5120	5120	5120	5120
Length (mm)	5134	5134	5164	5164	5164
Width (mm)	2316	2316	2382	2382	2382
Standard Weight (kg)	5080	5230	5580	5880	5880
Std. Tyre Size Front	420/70R28	420/70R28	16.9R28	16.9R28	16.9R28
Std. Tyre Size Back	18.4R38	18.4R38	20.8R38	20.8R38	20.8R38
Cab	TechCenter	TechCenter	TechCenter	TechCenter	TechCenter

The rear linkage can provide upto 8 ton lifting capacity on the 6920S, higher than most of the competition. Push-out hydraulic trailer hitch was standard on all machines and was essential to see the hook over the spool block.

Triple Link front suspension and cab suspension are most thought after and demand the higher premiums. Brakes usually last around 4000-6000 hours depending on the amount of road work covered by the machine.

Steering wheel was fully adjustable, with wiper switch and indicators within easy reach.

A combination of analogue and digital gauges make the dashboard simple and straight forward to read.

travel. In addition to this is the Hydraulic Cab Suspension (HCS) which further improved the operator environment. A 5.12m turning radius for all models is as good as any similar tractor of this size. While the brakes consist of oil cooled, self equalising and adjusting discs, front and back. Brakes usually last between 4000 and 6000 hours, so check their effectiveness.

CAB

The 20 series TechCenter cab is primarily an updated and improved version of the old 6000 series cab. The majority of the controls remain unchanged with a few improvements. The quality is still outstanding and is built to wear well and last. A new CommandArm control system moves all the vital controls to the seat armrest,

such as gear lever, linkage control, spools, hand throttle and PTO engagement. Left Hand Reverser shuttle remains in the same position underneath the steering wheel. Gauges are similar to previous models, an array of analogue dials and digital displays. The exterior of the cab received new fenders, roof and round plough lights over the 10 series design. The Hydraulic Cab Suspension (HCS) was welcomed by many operators and is a highly desired extra. Vision was excellent all round, with full glass front window and small cab pillars, providing 310° all round visibility. Noise levels could reach 72 dB(A) when under load, which many drivers insisted was louder than the previous range. Windscreen squeaks have been a problem in the past, but have all more than likely been solved by re-gluing.

DRIVING

Jumping aboard a 6920 is pretty much unhindered. Three well positioned wide steps lead to the flat floor cab, where the only obstacle is the passenger seat. The air seat is extremely comfortable, has plenty of adjustments and is likely to last a long time. The engine fires almost instantly, with the renowned JD bark. The clutch takes a moderate effort to depress and the gears on the PowerQuad Plus engage smoothly and precisely. The gear lever is a bit of a reach when in range E at its furthest from the driver, but the conveniently located toggle switch by the hand throttle makes changing gear a reduced stretch. The clutch engagement is very smooth, while the powershift change is quick and almost stepless.

The Left-Hand Reverser gave clutchless direction changes and a park-lock position on the AutoPowr models.

Although the side console appears dated, all controls remain in an accessible position.

Cab access is excellent, but is only slightly hindered if a suspended passenger seat is fitted.

The older 10 series received a facelift with many new features and futuristic, curvier styling. The new one piece fibreglass bonnet was a welcomed addition by most users for easier engine access.

Contacts

Ben Burgess – JD Dealers
East Anglia
Tel: 01603 628251
www.benburgess.co.uk

Farol Ltd – JD Dealers
Oxfordshire
Tel: 01844 278843
www.farol.co.uk

Rea Valley Tractors– JD Dealers
Pontesbury, Shrops

Tel: 01743 790801
www.rea-valley-tractors.co.uk

Nick Young Tractor Parts – New
and Used Spares
Holton Le Moor, Lincolnshire
Tel: 01673 828883

Brede Valley Tractors – JD
Specialists
Tel: 01424 882442

Steering is light and the lock makes the tractor very manoeuvrable. Brakes are very efficient and require little effort to bring the tractor to an abrupt stop. The dashboard dials make information very easy to read, while some of the warning lights can be hindered when the steering wheel is in certain positions. Pick-up hitch view is hindered, but can be seen when pushed out to its full extent. Overall the 6920 was an extremely pleasant drive, with very few bad points to be found.

VERDICT

At first the 20 series had a few teething problems which were soon rectified and many tractors already out there were sorted under warranty. Demand is high for these models and low houred tractors are particularly wanted for export. Resale values remain high and depreciation is very low making them a good investment. Expect to pay around the £30k mark for a low houred for a 2-3 year old tractor with low hours, while earlier, high houred machines make nearer £20k. ∎

How much	Parts Availability (Out of 5)							
Model	Year From	Year To	Mechanical	Bodywork	M	1	2	3
6520	2001	2006	5	5	£36750	£24500	£20000	£16500
6920S	2001	2006	5	5	£46000	£34,500	£28500	£23750

(Guide - M: Mint condition, 1: Excellent condition with no faults, 2: Tidy condition and useable, 3: Rough condition, for restoration or possibly breaking.)

New John Deere 6030 & 7030 Series tractors

We now review the German built John Deere 6030 and 7030 Series tractors ranging in power from 100 to 180hp. John Deere's latest generation of 110 to 203hp (Rated power with intelligent power management) tractors from Mannheim offers nine different models combining new Tier 3 engine technology with intelligent power management, field proven features and numerous ergonomic improvements.

Replacing the 6020 Series tractors, which were introduced in 2001, the new 6030 and 7030 Series Mannheim made tractors retain John Deere's proven full frame concept, modular transmission and lifelong components such as the Perma Clutch 2. The new range includes two brand new six-cylinder models, the 7430 and 7530, which extend the full frame concept for the first time into the 180 to 200hp bracket.

The new 6030 and 7030 Series tractors feature high pressure common rail PowerTech Plus diesel engines, which use the latest technology to deliver more power and usable torque. They are equipped with a variable geometry turbocharger for better fuel efficiency and engine responsiveness.

In addition, improved airflow and combustion efficiency are provided by four valves per cylinder in combination with a cooled exhaust gas recirculation system, to meet cleaner emission requirements without adversely affecting engine efficiency or fuel consumption.

All 30 Series premium tractors are available with the unique intelligent power management system, which generates extra engine power for PTO and transport applications – up to an additional 25hp depending on the model range. The extra power is provided during rear PTO operations when the tractor is moving and the PTO system detects a load, or during transport when travelling above 8.7mph (14kph).

A number of styling and ergonomic changes inside and outside the cab are designed to enhance operator comfort and help increase productivity. The newly contoured

New Tier 3 engines provide more power and fuel efficiency

bonnet gives it a narrower look and feel, while retaining the overall family appearance of the 7000 and 8000 Series tractors.

The new styled operator cab is the quietest on the market. For an easier reach from the steering wheel, the left hand reverser has been integrated into the newly designed dashboard, just

The new CommandCenter is a combines information and frequently used functions for optimum efficiency.

like the windshield wiper lever and the direction indicator, which is now selfcancelling as in a car. To provide the driver with a perfect view of the instrument panel from any position, the whole dashboard can now be moved telescopically.

A new one piece, right hand console incorporates the most ergonomically placed controls for a wide range of applications and operating requirements, including a choice of mechanical or electrical selective control valves on the right hand side. Front and rear PTO switches are now located directly in line and are in an easier location between the other controls, while the buttons for the Headland Management System (HMS) sequencing and AutoTrac assisted steering are integrated into the side of the electronic hitch control pod.

The new Command Center is a combination of information centre and set-up monitor in one large, full colour display. For frequently used functions such as the settings for the hitch, engine, transmission, HMS and SCVs there are shortcut keys on the control panel giving quick and direct access for setting changes.

Those functions, which are less often used, are featured in a single menu page, which can be accessed by pressing a menu button and using the rotating dial. Extra settings can be engaged via free programmable hotkeys on top of the CommandCenter, which also serves as an information centre to display relevant tractor data.

For instance, to operate the new Triple Link Suspension (TLS) plus system, the driver can choose one of three operating modes via the menu page, either Auto, Max or Manual. The system automatically produces a progressive spring adjustment to provide the best ride quality under extreme conditions. In Max mode,

maximum stiffness is achieved by raising the system's hydraulic pressure, an ideal solution for pallet work, for example, where placement accuracy is essential.

Transmission options remain the same as on previous models. The new 30 Series CommandARM option integrates the AutoPowr lever with the new right hand console, while for the ultimate in luxury a leather seat and leather steering wheel are also optionally available.

The 7430 and 7530, extend the 6000 Series full frame concept for the first time into the horsepower range between 180 and 200hp. These newly designed Mannheim made models have been developed particularly for the growing market segment of lightweight tractors in this power class and are built on a larger steel frame than the 6000 Series machines. This

provides an excellent power to weight ratio of 30kg/hp and a maximum power rating on the 7530 in excess of 200hp.

The combination of intelligent power management system, 6.6 tonne shipping weight and lift capacity of up to nine tonnes make these tractors ideal for a range of demanding transport and field applications. Both models feature a choice of PowerQuad Plus, Autoquad Plus with Eco Shift or Autopowr transmissions and are designed to accommodate the full range of AMS (Agricultural Management Solutions) GreenStar precision farming options.

Other features include a new rear axle and rear three-point hitch with Cat 3 linkage, and a 20 per cent larger cooling package specifically designed to allow maximum engine performance during the hottest conditions. Fuel tank capacity is 385 litres. ■

Technical specification

Four-cylinder, 4.5-litre PowerTech Plus engines

Model	Rated power (97/68 EC)	Rated power with IPM (97/68 EC)	Price
6230	100hp	110hp	£43,879
6330	110hp	120hp	£45,777
6430	120hp	130hp	£49,319

Six-cylinder, 6.8-litre PowerTech Plus engines

Model	Rated power (97/68 EC)	Rated power with IPM (97/68 EC)	Price
6530	120hp	140hp	£52,947
6630	130hp	150hp	£56,266
6830	140hp	165hp	£59,751
6930	155hp	180hp	£63,765
7430	165hp	190hp	£66,336
7530	180hp	203hp	£69,526

ATG Agricultural Contractors, Dorset

Adam Coleman is well known in the Dorset area for his contracting and farming business which extensively used John Deere equipment.

He currently has around 110 acres of finishing around for 180 beef cattle which includes 36 acres of barley for feed. The contracting side of the business employs 12 men, and the services include foraging (grass, whole-crop and maize), muck spreading, baling, ploughing and drilling, all mostly within a 10 mile radius of farm base.

At the top of fleet now stands two John Deere self-propelled forage harvesters, a 570hp 7700 and a new 625hp 7750i with ProDrive transmission, equipped with a 3m grass header and both six- and eight-row Kemper headers. Nine John Deere tractors from 135hp to 234hp chase up the foragers, including two 6820s, a 6920S, two 6830s, a 6930, a 7530 and not forgetting two 7920s, all bought from local dealer Colin Smart Agricultural Services, near Dorchester.

THREE FOR TWO

"I've been in the contracting business for 27 years, and have had most of John Deere's self-propelled forage harvester models since buying my first machine, a 5730, nearly 20 years ago," explains Adam Coleman.

"I've mostly run three John Deere foragers at any one time, with one used as a back-up machine when required, until 2008 – I'm now managing with one 7700 and the new 7750i, which has already done 500 hours

(to the first week of September) in its first season. With the maize harvest yet to start, I'll be keeping the 7700 for late cut silage and setting the new forager up for maize."

A whopping 7000 to 8000 acres of grass each year is likely to be harvested by ATG each year, plus 800 to 900 acres of wholecrop and around 800 acres of maize in addition. Although this figure has dropped dramatically in recent years as many local farmers have turned organic.

"When I had an initial demonstration of the new 7750i, I didn't really get too involved in the new technology, to be honest – I just thought, let's try the machine and see what it can do compared with the older models I was used to. The first thing I noticed straight away was how quiet it was in the cab, and there have been a number of other general improvements, for example to the feed rollers, the rotary screen and the chute, which seem to have made the forager a better machine all round."

STRAIGHTFORWARD AND USEFUL

"Once you get used to it, the new GreenStar satellite system and the 2600 touch screen display are very straightforward to use. It's particularly useful to be able to confirm the exact acreage we're working on, so the customer will accept our charges without quibbling."

This is an excellent feature that certainly is a must when everyone is trying to

be as efficient as possible and trying to keep costs as low as possible.

"The AutoLOC automatic length of cut system is just fantastic, and again quite simple to use. When you're cutting in good conditions, and you put it on the auto setting, you can watch the length of chop get longer as the grass moisture changes, as you work across the field. It does it all for you, it really does work brilliantly. It's particularly good with wholecrop, too."

"I think this is really a very good development, especially for contractors. All the harvest information is accurately recorded, so I can let my customers know exactly what I've been doing – I can print off the field area, litres of fuel used, moisture content, chop length over the whole field, and a detailed yield map. The technology is really telling my customers the true value of their forage as it comes off the field, so that if their cows are on a complete diet system, for example, they can make adjustments to the diet as required."

This type of information is especially important now with the rising cost of fuel, fertiliser and other inputs, as Mr Coleman's own monthly fuel costs have risen by as much as 60 per cent in the last year alone. Just as important is the way the system can show the yield variation across a field, as by referring to the yield maps, customers will be able to apply variable rate fertilisers if necessary, to really control their application costs and get the most from their forage. ■

Efficient harvesting - courtesy of John Deere.

New Series – new numbers

In the late autumn of 2008 John Deere introduced a new tractor range in Britain, the 5R Series and at the same time a new numbering system, making identification, power and specification level far simpler.

NEW NUMBERING SYSTEM

Take the model number 5100R for instance. The 5 denotes the Series, the secondary number 100 denotes the horsepower rating; in this case 100hp, the end letter is the specification level. R is for premium, T would be for tracked machine while N would be for narrow. In the United Kingdom and Ireland we will see tractors in both the R premium mid-spec and G standard range. There are other variants for row-crop and fruit growing operations but these would be generally for special order.

NEW 5R SERIES TRACTORS

The 90 to 100hp tractor is the largest power segment requirement for the UK and Ireland, the 5100 Series fits into this bracket nicely. The target market is the smaller livestock and mixed farm where a modern tractor is required for either cleaning out livestock buildings, winter feeding operations, some tillage work in spring and a tractor fully capable of hay and silage operations. Prior to the introduction of the 5R Series, tractors exceeding 100 horsepower had to be Tier III compliant, so with the introduction of the 5R tractors rated from 80–100hp these new tractors are fitted with Tier III A compliant engines. The major requirement of Tier III A regulations was to achieve a

40 per cent reduction in nitrogen oxide emissions. Effectively the engine is the same as in the 6030 Series, but is now a more modern unit with seven per cent more power than the previous 5200 Series which they replaced. Along with the increased power, the 5R Series has had to undergo further modifications. The new full-frame

chassis has been designed to allow a 20 per cent higher payload making it possible to fit and utilise heavier and larger implements. HMS (Headland Management System) is not fitted as standard on this tractor due to the type of work it was designed for, yet is available as an optional extra. Two transmission systems are available, either the basic 16/16 'PowrQuad Plus' or the 'AutoQuad Plus'. Both transmissions feature four ranges with four powershifting gears operating between 3.3kph and 40kph and are available with a 16/16 underdrive option that allows speeds as low as 1.5kph for vegetable operations. To aid handling and manoeuvrability, especially when using the front loader, both transmissions feature an electric power reverser.

CHOICE OF LOADERS

The 5100R can come delivered with a choice of three factory-fitted front loaders, or field-ready with a front hitch and PTO. A larger fuel tank of 150 litres is also optional over the standard 135-litre fuel tank.

An interesting feature on the 5100R is the 'active charge air cooler' with reverse fan. A rocker switch to the right-hand side of the operator can be switched to reverse the direction of the engine radiator fan to give a massive high blast of air lasting no more than 15 seconds which blows the radiator clean. If working in dry harvest or dusty tillage conditions the radiator can be cleaned with ease several times during a working day to avoid excessive heating and is one of the aids which helps reduce overall fuel consumption.

DRIVER'S VIEW

T&fT requested the services of a tractor operator who was more used to driving older tractors we asked for a brief report on how this modern machine compared. Our contact provided us with the following technical assessment: 'From opening the easily-accessible cab door and mounting the substantial steps, entry to the roomy cab was excellent. The operator's seat was quick and easy to adjust to suit the individual's height and weight. The steering

console was also easily adjustable to the operator's correct posture, thus providing good levels of operator comfort. All-round visibility in the 'TechCenter' was good, with cab corners having minimal obstruction giving a clear all-round view. There is a glass panel to aid front-end loader visibility. This glass panel has a blind which can be closed to help prevent dazzle from the sun when working in non-loader operations.

'The cab felt very airy, roomy, fresh and not confined. Both the rear view and cab mirrors were substantial, giving excellent vision when working in tight spaces such as cattle sheds and small farmyards, especially when on general loader duties. The steering console was well laid out with all controls at fingertip reach. All other controls were to the operator's right hand and easily accessible. On one-easy-to-grip joystick the operator could push buttons to move up and down through the transmission range, while on the same joystick the loader could be operated. Using the right hand on one lever all controls could be fully utilised while allowing the operator to keep the left hand on the steering wheel. The PTO for 540 and 540E had been relocated to a more accessible higher position to the right-hand side of the operator.'

IN CONCLUSION

The whole tractor is seen as compact yet strong, with good access for maintenance. Most service and filling points could be reached from ground level. Overall, the cab (to which there is fairly easy access) is uncluttered by unnecessary or bulky switches and levers. From a standing start acceleration is smooth. Electronic forward/reverse seems effortless. For the smaller farm this is an excellent machine in the 100 (and below) horsepower bracket. ∎

The 7430 and 7530 with 'AutoPowr' transmission with electronic 'SCVS' equals the E-Premium with full electronic capabilities. 'AutoPowr' transmission is operated by one lever which allows the operator to select a specific speed enabling the engine and transmission to work together to keep the tractor in balance. The new models are rated at 165 and 180hp, rising to 200 and 215hp for tractors fitted with Intelligent Power Management (IPM). These tractors, equipped with an integrated, high-power electric distribution system, will be available in the United Kingdom and Ireland in late spring 2009.

A generator provides the power for electrically-driven components such as the airconditioning compressor, engine cooling fan and air brake compressor, resulting in increased engine performance and better fuel efficiency. This design is the first example of electrical power being utilised to improve overall tractor efficiency, with the 'E' power management system controlling the various component drives at the appropriate time. The precise engine cooling fan speed is regulated by the system according to engine temperature, which tends to lead to higher power levels at lower engine speeds for improved fuel economy.

PORTABLE POWER!

Incorporated in the rear end of the E-Premium tractors are two external power sockets. The red socket is for 400 volts whilst the blue socket is for 230 volts. These two outlets can allow the operator to boil a kettle, operate a welder, angle grinder or even to operate a sheep-shearing unit anywhere around the farmstead or out in the fields. The tractor can become a portable power unit.

Via the Command Centre the radiator on the E-Premium can be cleaned quickly by operating the easy-clean radiator, active-charged air cooler grille cooling system which has a reverse fan to give a high blast of air to clean out all dust.

The new 8R series feature more power and a completely new CommandView II cab.

The new 8R series

John Deere's 8000 series has seen various improvements over the years, but the cab and technology has remained primarily unchanged in recent years. But 2010 saw the new CommandView II cab introduced which will feature a new CommandARM with colour display in addition to a new track system capable of traveling at 42kph. Howard Sherren travels to Germany to discover the new range.

The John Deere 8030 series range of high-horse tractors was one of the first to receive '30 Series' status over four years ago and the design was still heavily influenced by the original 8000s which appeared in 1994. When launched, the 8000s were far superior to many comparative machines, with new levels of comfort in the single-door CommandView cab and clean-cut styling. With 10, 20 and 30 series updates already in place, John Deere has gone for a new numbering system with the 8R series which will hopefully be easier to understand for the Deere outsiders, and likely to confuse existing customers.

Described as "Delivering Performance that Endures" the 8Rs consist of five wheeled models and three tracked versions. The smallest model in the previous tracked 30 series has been dropped through lack of demand and a new 380hp flagship introduced. For those not aware of the new numbering system, the first number indicates the series, which is followed by the engine output and finally includes the capability where 'R' stands for the Premium specification and 'T for the all-important tracks.

POWERTECH PLUS
In addition to the new model range comes more power, although the front half of the tractor remains relatively unchanged. Fitted with John Deere's 9- litre PowerTech

Plus engine, to meet Tier III specifications it also incorporates a Variable Geometry Turbocharger (VGT) and Exhaust Gas Recirculation (EGR). In addition they can utilise around 9 to 10 per cent of the power bulge allowing the flagship 8345, for example, to increase its power from 345 horses to an impressive 380hp. Intelligent Power Management (IPM) also provides up to 35 extra horses for stationary PTO and transport applications, not only that but it can achieve a maximum IPM of 47hp at 1,900rpm. So far the new engines have been found to be just as efficient as the previous engines, though tracked users will be very pleased to hear they have 54 per cent more fuel capacity, so at 758 litres there will be even longer periods between fill-ups. ➥

The range now spans from the 245hp 8245R, up to the flagship 345hp 8345R.

TRANSMISSION AND AIRCUSHION

Transmission-wise the machines have been pretty much unchanged although they offergreater choice. The existing 16 forward and 5 reverse PowerShift transmission has beenretained and is available on everything apart from the flagship 8345. The legendary AutoPowr IVT transmission is now available on all models with right or left hand (only on wheeled models) shuttle control, also offering speeds from 50m per hour, up to 42kph – a 24 per cent increase.

An exciting new development on the 8RT is that speeds of 42kph are now possible on a tracked machine which is certainly an exciting new territory to be in and unseen to date. This has been made possible by an all-new track from the bottom up including a new AirCushion track suspension system. Each track has one cushion bag and one track tensioner per track which helps to provide greater comfort and safety allowing the machine to travel at greater speeds. This was helped further by lengthening the track by a further 254mm which distributes the weight better and increases the foot print to help lower compaction. Two sizes of track are available, 635mm (25") and 762mm (30") in addition to a choice of two widths of mid-rollers and a wider drive wheel.

The old outboard planetary drives have been banished making way for inboard versions and the whole track unit can be removed from the machine simply by unbolting it and lifting off the machine with a forklift. Setting the track width has never been simpler!

Existing 8030	New 8R	New 8R IPM	Price
8130 (225hp)	8245R (245hp)	8245R (280hp)	£111,328
8230 (250hp)	8270R (270hp)	8270R (305hp)	£120,007
8330 (280hp)	8295R (295hp)	8295R (330hp)	£129,040
8430 (305hp)	8320R (320hp)	8320R (355hp)	£145,297
8530 (330hp)	8345R (345hp)	8345R (380hp)	£157,239

8030 Track	New 8RT Track	New 8RT Track IPM	Price
8230T (240hp)	-	-	-
8330T (280hp)	8295RT (295hp)	8295RT (330hp)	£176,320
8430T (305hp)	8320RT (320hp)	8320RT (355hp)	£192,559
-	8345RT (345hp)	8345RT (380hp)	£204,519

With Intelligent Power Management (IPM) the flagship 8345R can top 380 horses.

There are three tracked models, the 8295RT, 8320RT and 8345RT which are now capable of 42kph thanks to track suspension.

Redesigned tracks are longer and now include an airbag to provide suspension. Available in two track widths, the complete units can be removed simply by unbolting and lifting-off with a forklift.

COMMANDVIEW II

Probably the most significant new development on the 8R series is the all-new CommandView II cab which boasts 10 per cent more space with better visibility from 7 per cent more glass. Also after a demand from customers, four times the storage space of the previous cab has been added by removing the right-hand console completely. The new cab has been dubbed a "True mobile office" which now features automotive technology to improve the design, for example the glass is fixed in with Urethane adhesive to avoid the chances of dust and noise leaking into the cab.

The ClimaTrak air-conditioning has also been improved by moving the system back into the roof from under the cab floor, increasing airflow by 30 per cent and optimising the air-flow towards the driver. The air filter is now in easy access at the side of the roof and can be easily removed from the cab steps and is less likely to suck in disturbed dust. Continuing with the roof, a radio is now standard which will feature USB and MP3 capabilities with four speakers. Premium models however will also have Bluetooth , a CD player and a subwoofer - impressive!

When it comes to lighting there are now three lighting packages, standard, deluxe and premium which offers a stadium-style illumination with no dead zones. All lights will now be fixed to reduce the parts required and avoid damage out in the field. Lastly on-top of the roof, as part of an original promotion, each tractor will be Autotrac ready and feature a StarFire bracket as standard to make guidance even easier.

COMMANDARM

The original 8000 series had five digital displays to keep an eye on for vital information. Not only did this take up space

but things could be missed. Now all of these have been incorporated into two displays, one mounted on the front pillar and a new 7" colour display mounted on the armrest and known as the CommandCentre.

In addition to improve space, visibility and operator environment, all the right-hand side console has been moved to the armrest and all vital features can be controlled at the tip of a finger. The CommandARM can now control hydraulic and transmission settings, along with four-wheel drives, diff-lock and even the radio and climate control through a thumb wheel and push buttons. Combined with the new light charcoal grey interior and optional leather covered ComfortCommand seat, the working environment appears to be considerably improved now John Deere has addressed many of the existing problems expressed by users.

Prices start at £111,328 for the base 245hp 8245R, rising to £157,239 for the flagship 345hp 8345R. Tracked examples will start at £176,320 for the 8295RT, whilst the 8345RT will come in at £204,519. The tractors were revealed to farmers at Agritechnica in November 2009. ∎

The front of the tractor remains primarily unchanged, but the cab is completely new with a bright new interior colour.

A new 7" colour screen will provide all the vital information and displays for the setting up of the tractor.

The side console has now been completely moved to the armrest which helps to improve storage and visibility.

EIGHT GREAT MAGAZINES FROM KELSEY PUBLISHING

OVER 1000 TRACTORS AND PARTS FOR SALE

MONTHLY
Passionate about tractors and the World's best-selling magazine for all enthusiasts, collectors and restorers.
www.tractor-and-machinery.com

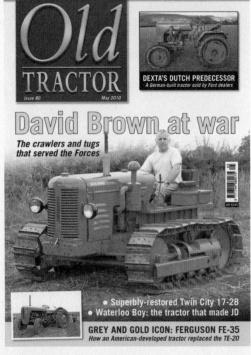

MONTHLY
Full of in-depth features, packed with rare photos, concentrating on vintage through to classic tractors.
www.oldtractor.co.uk

BI-MONTHLY
The magazine and club for lovers of Ford, Fordson and New Holland tractors, Britain and Ireland's most popular tractors.
www.fordfordsonassociation.com

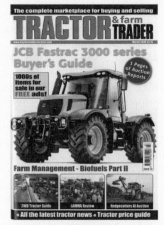

BI-MONTHLY
Catering for all levels if interest from the farmer to the contractor to the agriculture dealer.
www.tractorandfarmtrader.com

MONTHLY
Interested in diggers, dumpers and trucks or want to buy one? This title is just what you are looking for!
www.cpmmag.co.uk

BI-MONTHLY
This independent Ferguson and Massey Ferguson magazine is totally devoted to the red and grey tractor.
www.classicmassey.co.uk

MONTHLY
Takes you into the fascinating engineering hobby of stationary engines – the really low-cost entry-level hobby.
www.stationary-engine-magazine.co.uk

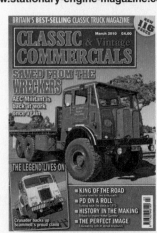

MONTHLY
The best-selling magazine dedicated to heavy commercial vehicles from the heyday of road haulage.
www.cvcmag.co.uk

For latest prices and subs deals phone 01959 541444 or visit the websites

Kelsey Publishing Ltd, Cudham Tithe Barn, Berry's Hill, Cudham, Kent TN16 3AG

Tel: 01959 541444   Fax: 01959 541400   Email: subs@kelsey.co.uk   kelsey website: www.kelsey.co.uk